THE SOCIAL IMPACT OF CYBERNETICS

The Social Impact of

Contributors

John Diebold
Charles R. Dechert
Robert Theobald
Ulric Neisser
Marshall McLuhan
Hyman G. Rickover
Maxim W. Mikulak
John J. Ford

Cybernetics

Edited by

CHARLES R. DECHERT

UNIVERSITY OF NOTRE DAME PRESS

Notre Dame 1966 London

ACKNOWLEDGMENT

Maxim W. Mikulak's "Cybernetics and Marxism-Leninism" appeared in the *Slavic Review,* XXIV, 3 (September, 1965), 450–465. Charles R. Dechert's "The Development of Cybernetics" appeared in *The American Behavioral Scientist,* VIII, 10 (June, 1965), 15–20. Hyman G. Rickover, who holds the copyright, granted permission to print "A Humanistic Technology."

UNIVERSITY OF NOTRE DAME PRESS

Notre Dame, Indiana

Library of Congress Catalog Number: 66-24925

Manufactured in the United States of America

Foreword

THE ESSAYS IN THIS VOLUME HAVE BEEN SElected from among the papers presented at a symposium on the social impact of cybernetics held in Washington, D.C., in November, 1964, under the joint sponsorship of Georgetown University, American University, and The George Washington University. The symposium formed part of the 175th Anniversary Year Program of Georgetown University and was set up with the cooperation of the newly formed American Society for Cybernetics.

These meetings were not directed at the scientific and technical aspects of communications and control systems, but rather at the implications of cybernetic technologies and modes of thought for our understanding of men in society, and their significance for social development. An effort was made to bring together scholars in the humanities and social sciences, physicists and engineers, members of the business community and public officials. The bond uniting the participants was a common active interest in communication and control processes and the impact of cybernetics-based technologies on culture and the human condition.

A common theme characterizes the studies published in this volume as it characterized the discussions at the Georgetown symposium. Our increasing ability to understand and control complex dynamic processes, including social processes, has profound implications for men's image of themselves and of the world they live in. Cybernetics has required that we examine ever more carefully the criteria of relevance that govern perception and the values that govern action. As these essays make abundantly clear, the ability to organize rationally large-scale technical and social processes has already radically changed man's milieu and produced a grave challenge to many existing institutions.

From many different viewpoints, the authors raise the ethical question: "What values will be served by cybernetic technologies?" They may be used to impose the dead hand of uniformity and restrictive political controls, or they may be used to stimulate cooperative and mutually supportive institutions that combine a high level of economic well-being and the opportunity for human creativity with respect for traditional cultures and personal freedom. Determining the human values to be served by cybernetics may well be the most critical ethical challenge of this generation.

CHARLES R. DECHERT,
Editor

Contents

GOALS TO MATCH OUR MEANS

John Diebold

WE ARE LIVING IN AN ERA SO DIFFERENT FROM that in which we were born that we do not yet comprehend the nature or magnitude of the change that is taking place. When we talk of the problems of cybernetics and society, we should think in world terms, for this is in fact a worldwide development, and depending upon the culture, depending upon the economy, depending upon the outlook and the philosophy, the phenomenon is being approached in many different ways around the world.

The industrial revolution is finally over. At some time in the last twenty or thirty years, the seeds of the next era were sown. We have but to look about us to see these seeds growing. The shape of this new age is still unknowable. The variety of the problems facing us in the next twenty years more than equal those that men have faced over the past two hundred. Julian Huxley wrote:

> It is an exciting fact that man, after he appeared to be dethroned from his supremacy, demoted from his central position in the universe to the insignificant inhabitant of a small, outlying planet of one among six millions of stars, has now become reinstated in a key position, one of the rare spearheads or torchbearers or trustees of advance in the cosmic process of evolution. The present is a challenging moment.

To begin with, we should be absolutely clear about the meaning of the machines and the technology that constitute the applications of cybernetics. They are agents for social change. One has but to examine the phrase "the industrial revolution" to realize this.

The steam engine, the cotton gin, the railway, the power loom—these were truly revolutionary machines. These inventions did more than change the economics of the time. Taken together, they changed the entire character of our life on this planet. They changed the environment of mankind. They created problems that are still with us. Once we understand this fact, we begin to realize just how difficult it is to comprehend the change that engulfs us today. We begin to understand that our first concern must be to formulate the questions before we can hope to forge the answers.

Among the chief of these problems is the condensing time scale—the rate at which events are happening. We still have the age-old problem of understanding the true meaning of events. Do we see in an invention such as Gutenberg's press the means of producing splendid copies of illuminated manuscripts? Many people did. Do we view electricity and the automobile as rich men's toys? Most people did. Do we consider the computer as a calculating engine, something useful only in a few laboratories? Understanding the meaning of the developments about us is crucial to the problems of assessing what is going to happen as a result of our new technology. In assessing cybernetics, it is especially important to look in a fresh manner at what appears to be happening. All too often one will look at the machine—here the computer—and draw conclusions in terms of human and social and economic consequences. But the computer is not at all at the heart of cybernetics. The heart of the field is something that can sound very esoteric; it is nonetheless of enormous importance. It is a newly found ability to understand the nature of information, and with it the ability to build machine systems which can handle information, communicate it, and do things with it. The computer is only the first of many families of machines. We are, for example, beginning to have a whole new family of machines to translate language.

The history is that the machines get smaller and less costly and more reliable. It is useless to look at today's machines and then to make economic and social calculations about their future. In 1946 people were making statements that 12 computers would do all the work needed to be done by computers in the United States. In 1947 the estimate was increased to 50. Today we have twenty thousand computers in operation and we shall double that figure very shortly. We must look to the future because we cannot understand our technology's effects on people and on society if we look only at the present. We must try to anticipate and understand the form of the future. Understanding can, and must, outpace what we are yet able to analyze with mathematical precision.

The nature and speed of the changes in our day produce all kinds of new problems and complicate old problems. We live now in a qualitively different world, not simply one which has changed in numbers, not simply a mechanized, computerized version of yesterday's world. Today the buttons push themselves! Then, too, the tasks that we put to the machines are also very different from the tasks of the past. It will soon be a truism to say that we should all engage ourselves in the problems produced by this world and that we should all engage ourselves in the process of trying to formulate the questions to be asked and then try to seek the answers. This is the most exciting development we have had in history, and it is the prime development of our times.

The problem of formulating the right questions is not only one of weighing the alternatives but one of identifying the issues. The first things to come to mind are, of course, the human consequences of our new era, the consequences for manpower, for employment. Another tier of problems linked to these concerns the kind of system conceptually available for the distribution of the products of a computerized society as the human effort needed to produce these products decreases. Extremely perplexing problems, for example, are arising from determining the meaning of a productivity measure. In a category by themselves are the problems of education and learning, among them those of equipping people for changing jobs in a changing world, and particularly of that increasingly important aspect of life we call leisure. Such a change of emphasis will require modifications in our educational structure and outlook.

The problems that I have been describing have all resulted from environmental changes. There are even more fundamental problems, problems which up to now have received virtually no attention. These, for the most part, concern man in himself and in his political society. As Bernard Baruch writes in *The Philosophy for Our Time,* "Where we once could let nature take its course, we must now be able to think things out, and that is a terrible thing." We can—and must—do as Mr. Baruch proposes. We must engage ourselves and see that others are engaged in the problem.

Another fundamental problem concerns man's concept of himself. Each time a major scientific innovation has been made, we find that our own concept of ourselves becomes more profound. It changes; it becomes more true. Each time we change the scientific understanding of our world, we begin to have to face anew the question of the nature of mankind. We now have an overwhelming reason for again examining our concept of ourselves. We have already in the laboratory machines that behave with intelligence. Only a few years ago the problem of machines that exhibit intelligent behavior could be discussed—and dismissed—in cavalier fashion. But the answer is already here. Intelligent behavior on the part of machine systems has already been exhibited in the laboratory. What, we must now seriously ask, are the characteristics that are truly, uniquely human? Each time in the past when we have been forced to a revaluation of ourselves in the light of new knowledge and new processes, we have emerged with a far more profound realization of the true nature of mankind. I cannot but believe that this will happen again since the problem is again with us in a new and different and challenging form.

Then there is that complex of problems related to man's order—his political, economic, social order here on earth. Why is it that when we speak of the human consequences of technology, both individually and collectively, we seem to exhibit a certain uneasiness? One need only look back to the beginning of the era that has just ended—the industrial revolution—to find some of the reasons why we feel this way about technology. At four o'clock in the morning 150 years ago one could find groups of eight- and ten- and twelve-year-old children trudging to work through the landscape from hell that technology had created in the midlands of England. Out of this phenomenon came much of today's world—directly out of it came Karl Marx's answer, his baleful answer, to our shatteringly inadequate method of coping with technological change.

Today we again are faced in a very different way with the problem of fundamental changes in man's order on earth. If we make our approach on the basis of saying that we are in a capitalist, free enterprise society and we want it to stay just the way it is, what hope do we have of preserving that society for our children? Very little.

The only conceivable way of trying to preserve the good things we have is to realize that our whole approach must be one of understanding in really profound terms the nature of the change and of forging a new form of society. We must lead the way, and not be dragged, into this new era. We discovered how to make the enterprise system dynamic by making it responsive to the times, something that plays a positive role that is attractive to the world—and to ourselves.

We can only play this role if we respond to change. There is no question whatever of perpetuating old forms and old institutions through the device of refusing to respond. All about us we see the beginnings of a world meeting change. Vatican Council II is a striking example of coping with the challenges and the necessities of the new age. We find aspects of this general problem of adaptation being attempted in many parts of the world. Even though the way we must change is not yet clear, it is imperative that we engage ourselves in this problem in a way that benefits mankind.

Clearly, we are faced today with the most profound issues of public policy. Yet we should not too readily equate such policy with the government action. We tend all too easily to ignore a problem in the hope that a government department will be created, or at the very least a study committee.

The private sector should properly concern itself with issues of public policy. Yet, we in the private sector have largely failed to rise to the new challenges that lie before us. I think it notable, for example, that the foundations have given virtually no attention whatever to the problems posed by what we may truly call the cybernetic revolution.

We tend, as I have said, to feel that this area of thought and action should be left to government. To be sure, the role of government will change, and many of these problems are properly the concern of government action—action much more effective and extensive than we have experienced thus far. But these are not problems to be left solely to government; they are problems for all sectors of our society.

The problem of identifying and understanding

goals to match the new means that technology provides us is the central problem of our time—one of the greatest problems in human history. Its solution can be one of the most exciting and one of the most important areas for human activity.

And the time is now.

THE DEVELOPMENT OF CYBERNETICS

Charles R. Dechert

THE TERM "CYBERNETICS" DERIVES FROM THE Greek word *kybernetes,* which means steersman. Plato uses it to describe the prudential aspect of the art of government.[1] Ampère in his *Essay on the Philosophy of Science* used the term *cybernétique* for the science of civil government.[2] The Latin term *gubernator* is derived from the Greek, and hence also our word governor. In English we use the term governor in at least two ways: first in the traditional sense of a public steersman or political decision-maker; second to refer to the self-adjusting valve mechanism on a steam engine which keeps the engine at a constant speed under varying conditions of load. In the steam engine governor, a valve linked to the engine's output shaft increases steam flow into the engine as the output speed decreases, raising the speed to the level desired, or reduces steam flow if the speed exceeds the pre-established level. Maxwell analyzed this control phenomenon mathematically in his paper on governors published in 1868.[3] What is essentially involved in steering behavior or control behavior of the type illustrated by the steam engine governor is a feedback loop through which the output of the system is linked to its input in such a way that variations in output from some pre-established or "programmed" norm results in compensatory behavior that tends to restore the system output to that norm.

An analogous process occurs in organisms subjected to internal or external changes that might disrupt metabolism. By the turn of the century physiologists such as Claude Bernard were fully aware of this process of "homeostasis" whereby an organism acts so as to restore its internal equilibrium. Cannon's *Wisdom of the Body* is a classical exposition of these phenomena in the autonomic processes of men. The self-regulatory aspect of neurophysiological phenomena was treated by such men as Sherrington in his work on reflexes, McCulloch in his analysis of neural networks, and Rosenblueth in his studies of psychomotor disorders. By the early 1940's physicists, electrical engineers, and mathematicians were at work on servo-mechanisms, self-regulating systems that could be used for such military purposes as gun laying. A broad range of disciplines had been at work on analogous problems of self-regulation. Institutionally, the interdisciplinary study of self-regulation in the animal and the machine began at a meeting held in New York in 1942, sponsored by the Josiah Macy Foundation.

BEHAVIOR AND PURPOSE

One result was a paper on "Behavior, Purpose and Teleology" which serves as a watershed in which the breadth of the analogy was realized.[4] In 1943 *Philosophy of Science* published this article by Norbert Wiener, Arturo Rosenblueth, and Julian Bigelow. The authors distinguish between the "functional analysis" of an entity and a "behavioristic approach." In the former ". . . the main goal is the intrinsic organization of the entity studied, its structure and its properties. . . . The behavioristic approach consists in the examination of the output of the object and of the relations of this output to the input." Wiener in his subsequent works largely restricted himself to ". . . the behavioristic method of study [which] omits the specific structure and intrinsic organization of the object." The authors assign the term "servomechanism" to designate machines with "intrinsic purposeful behavior." Purposeful behavior is directed at ". . . a final condition in which the behaving object reaches a definite correlation in time or space with respect to another object or event. All purposeful behavior may be considered to require negative feedback," that is ". . . the behavior of an object is controlled by the margin of error at which the object stands at a given time with reference to a relatively specific goal." The authors conclude on the note that "purposefulness [is] a concept necessary for the understanding of certain modes of behavior. . . ," and define teleology as "purpose controlled by feedback." The authors reject the concept of teleology as implying a "cause subsequent in time to a given effect."

In this model the key elements of self-regulation were reduced to a form amenable to mathematical analysis, and the knotty problem of consciousness so relevant to human behavior was bypassed. The novelty of this mode of conceptualizing purposive behavior lies in its implicit distinction between energy and information. " 'Control' is a special kind of relation between two machines or parts of machines, such that one part regulates the operation of the other. . . . The essential point is that the source of energy is dissociated from the source of instructions."[5] The transformation of relatively high energic inputs into goal-oriented outputs is subject to relatively low energies characterized by a formal content whose programmed interaction with these high energies produces the purposive transformation.

The principal characteristic of a self-regulating system is the presence of a control loop whereby system comportment may be modified on the basis of information inputs regarding performance and the comparison of performance with a criterion value. The control loop may be a "closed loop" existing within the boundaries of the system, or it may be an "open loop." In open loop feedback, part of the control information flow takes place outside the system boundary. The interaction of a self-regulating system with its external environment characteristically involves an open loop. Effector elements on the system boundary manipulate the environment to achieve certain objectives. Sensor elements (receptors) perceive environmental changes which are transmitted to a decision-making element that compares this percept with the objective and transmits new orders to the effector elements in terms of the difference between objective and achievement.

Basically, self-regulation requires a functional distinction between perception, decision-making, and action. This is normally achieved by a structural distinction between perceptor elements, control elements and effector elements in the system. Behaviorally, a system may be defined as a "black box" characterized by a given set or range of inputs and outputs. Adequate knowledge of any system requires both structural-functional analysis and behavioral analysis. Where very large numbers of inputs and/or outputs are involved or where the system is composed of a large number of components, statistical techniques are required and behaviors are analyzed probabilistically. It is entirely possible, of course, that structurally diverse systems may effect identical transformations, and that structurally identical systems of a sufficient degree of complexity may produce very different outputs on the basis of identical inputs. The "sensitivity" of a system refers to the degree of departure of the output from a programmed norm that invokes an adjustive response. "Rapidity of response" refers to the speed with which a given system will correct behavior that does not correspond to the norm. "Stability" refers to the ability of a system to maintain a given behavioral posture over time. Normally there is a rather close formal relation between these aspects of system behavior. The more sensitive a system, the less likely it is to be stable over a broad range of inputs and outputs. The more rapid the response of the system to an error signal, the more likely it is to overshoot the norm—to overadjust, and so invoke a counter-adjustment, to overadjust, and so forth. This behavior may lead to oscillation destructive of the entire system.

INFORMATION AND MESSAGES

It is clear at this point of our discussion that control involves the communication of information. In an operational sense, information is that which can or does influence the comportment of another. Information is conveyed as a message, that is, as a configuration of signal elements borne by a medium having actual or potential meaning for the recipient (destination). By the late 1920's communications engineers, concerned with the problems of interference (noise) and channel capacity, had begun to develop measures of information.[6] This work culminated in 1948 in a paper of Shannon entitled, "The Mathematical Theory of Communication."[7] Shannon's study does not concern itself with meaning, that is, with the semantic aspects of communication but with the technical problems of the accuracy of transmission of various types of signals. Clearly, the purely technical problems of coding, transmitting, and decoding signal sequences are of critical importance in designing and understanding self-regulating systems. The actual comportment of such systems, however, is a function of the semantic content of these signal sequences. The "quantity of information" as a measure of the improbability of a signal sequence has no *necessary* relation to the amount of semantic information conveyed by a statement.[8]

In 1948 Wiener published *Cybernetics or Control and Communication in the Animal and the Machine* which formalized much of the thinking up to that time and suggested potentially fruitful areas for further inquiry. With the quantification of signal transmission and the formalization of control system theory a new and broadly applicable science of communications and control had become a reality. In its strict applications, communications and control theory has become a major factor in contemporary technology and lies at the base of the "second industrial revolution." In the "first industrial revolution" prime movers largely replaced human energy while men performed a control function. Under automation, process and production *control* is relegated to servomechanisms while the human operator programs, monitors, and maintains the automated system.

SCOPE OF CYBERNETICS

In the United States, scientists and engineers working in the theory and applications of self-regulation tend to avoid the term cybernetics, which deals to a considerable degree with isomorphisms among the various types of self-regulating systems. Since only a very limited range of systems and communications processes are presently amenable to mathematical formalization and manipulation, there has been a tendency to institutionalize fairly narrow disciplines concerned with limited formal or material applications of these concepts, such as computer engineering, bionics, and control systems engineering. In the Soviet Union, on the other hand, the term cybernetics is used quite broadly, ". . . not as the doctrine of Wiener, Shannon, Ashby, *et al.,* but as the general science of the control over complex systems, information, and communications. . . ."[9] Elsewhere in the Soviet literature we find cybernetics defined as ". . . the new science of purposeful and optimal control over complicated processes and operations which take place in living nature, in human society, and in industry."[10]

Cybernetics extends the circle of processes

> which can be controlled—this is its special property and merit. It can help control life activity in living nature, purposeful work of organized groups of people, and the influence of man on machines and mechanisms.
>
> We shall divide cybernetics into three large subdivisions: theoretical cybernetics which includes mathematical and philosophical problems; the cybernetics of control systems and means which includes the problems of collecting, processing, and output of information, and also the means for electronic automation; finally, the field of the practical application of the methods and means of cybernetics in all fields of human activity.[11]

Many of the basic concepts of this science are relevant to an understanding of social groups. Norbert Wiener realized their applicability and suggested many insightful applications, but was concerned about potential abuses owing to the complexity of social processes and the limited applicability of existing methods of mathematical analysis. On the other hand, he also pointed out that the application of cybernetic concepts to society does not require that social relations be mathematicizable *in esse,* but only *in posse*—that is, the conceptual clarification of the formal aspects of social relations can make a positive contribution to the science of society.[12]

More recent definitions of cybernetics almost invariably include social organizations as one of the categories of system to which this science is relevant.[13] Indeed, Bigelow has generalized to the extent of calling cybernetics the effort to understand the behavior of complex systems.[14] He pointed out that cybernetics is essentially interdisciplinary and that a focus at the systems level, dependent upon mixed teams of professionals in a variety of sciences, brings one rapidly to the frontiers of knowledge in several areas. This is certainly true of the social sciences. The term "cybernetics" is used here in the more extended sense discussed above. It is entirely appropriate that this should be done, not only because of the traditional political and social connotation of the term governance, but because of the role played by the social and behavioral sciences in the explication and development of models of social control and decision-making. The first modern calculating machine was made by Charles Babbage, whose classic study (*On the Economy of Machinery and Manufactures*) was published in 1832 and anticipated by fifty years or more the beginnings of scientific management.[15] Organizational theory, political science, cultural anthropology and social psychology have for many years analyzed social groups as complex communications nets characterized by a multiplicity of feedback loops. Organizational decision-making was given a quantitative base, again at the time of World War II, by the development of the techniques of operations research. Von Neumann and Morgenstern succeeded in analyzing strategic optima in certain types of decision processes. In 1936 Leontief produced the first input-output matrix. Von Bertalanffy has pointed out analogies (isomorphisms) characterizing all systems, including social systems.[16]

ROLE OF COMPUTERS

Let us now examine certain aspects of the popular view of cybernetics. In one view, cybernetics is identified with the development and use of large digital computers. Computers are, of course, of fundamental importance to cybernetics, first because they embody so much communications and control technology, and second because they oblige us to sort out vague ideas and feelings from clearly formulated univocal ideas and relations if we wish to manipulate them by machine, and finally because once ideas are clarified the machine permits the rapid execution of long and detailed logical operations otherwise beyond human capability. In many cases these logical operations performed by machine permit a rationality in decision-making or precision of control hitherto unattainable. Until a few years ago it was impossible to compare very large numbers of decisional alternatives to find an optimum. Decision techniques and aids such as linear and dynamic programming, critical path analysis, large-scale input-output matrices, network analysis, factor analysis, simulation, and so forth are largely dependent upon computers.

Computer technology, of course, lies at the base

of the automatic factory, of sophisticated inventory control systems, and of the increasing automation of routine paper work. Fundamentally, any information-handling operation that can be reduced to rule and rote is amenable to computer performance. Considered abstractly, this means that virtually every human job activity that does not require intellectual or artistic creativity or some human emotivity in its performance is potentially susceptible of automation. Under our existing institutional "rules of the game" the only limiting factor will be the cost of the machine as opposed to the cost of people.

It now seems increasingly likely that computer networks will be formed, first on a local, then a regional, and finally a national scale, which will make unused computer capacity available, perhaps on a rental basis—and which as a unit will be capable of data processing tasks of hitherto inconceivable magnitude. Eventually each citizen may have access to computers and a vast complex of data storage centers on a rental-use basis. Computers might be used to handle such routine chores as tallying adding machine tapes, making out Christmas mailing lists and preparing income tax returns. At a more sophisticated level perhaps our citizen may use his machine to analyze interpersonal relations in his office sociometrically in order to optimize strategies for personal effectiveness. He may have access to a wide range of factual or bibliographic information; he may, perhaps, run machine searches of newspaper files or gather genealogical data. From a purely practical economic viewpoint there would be obvious benefits to American business to be gained from centralized insurance files, credit reports, accident reports, academic and job records, public opinion surveys, and so forth. All of these would enhance predictability, and so also increase businesses' capacity for rational decision-making. The principal question that will arise in this process of increasing centralized information storage concerns the values in terms of which the information will be utilized in making decisions. Profit maximization? a politically imposed values-mix? or might new institutional forms permit more decentralized decision on the basis of widely varying criteria? In the not very distant future some hard public decisions must be made regarding who shall have access to what information and for what purposes, and perhaps as to what types of information may legitimately be collected and employed.

APPLICATIONS TO SOCIAL SYSTEMS

Let us return to our basic model of a self-regulating system, examine some of its fundamental operations a little more closely, and try to see wherein it is applicable to the study of social relations.

A system is an organized collection of interrelated elements characterized by a boundary and functional unity. The concept of system emphasizes the reality of complex relational networks and permits the analysis of mutual causal processes involving large numbers of interacting entities. Although systems of ideas and systems of symbols play a critical role in human society, we shall here treat of social systems as real composite entities in continuing self-regulated interaction with their environment(s). Social systems comprise every level of complexity from the family or primary work group through large-scale formal organizations to the nation-state or even the whole human race conceived of as an interacting human community. Primary groups and ultimately all groups are composed of self-regulating persons as their components. Large social systems normally consist of functional groups as their component subsystems. The integrated activity of large social groupings is the product of effective internal communication and a willingness on the part of decision-makers in their component social subsystems and ultimately of their component persons to respond in a predictable and programmed manner to a defined range of perceptual inputs.

Fundamentally, a model of self-regulation requires a functional distinction between perception, decision-making, and action. This is normally achieved by a structural distinction between receptor elements, decision-making elements, and effector elements in the system. As social systems increase in size and complexity, these functions and the related communications .functions tend to become concentrated in component social subsystems.[17]

If we apply these basic concepts in a very much simplified way to the political sphere they may help to systematize certain basic relations that are the traditional matter of political science, such as the constitution and the separation of powers.[18] Basically, a constitution is a program defining the nature (activities) and interrelations of the formal loci of political power. The outputs of the political system are enforceable laws defining the interrelations of persons and groups within the society. Demands on the political system are communicated by petition, by representatives of organized groups, by publicists, and other means including elections. Legislative decisions are made in the form of laws and resolutions. The executive puts the laws into effect and the judiciary serves a control function by comparing specific individual actions with the law that programs such action. Even judicial review in the United States is fundamentally a comparison of legislative action (output) with a constitutional norm.

Similarly in the conduct of foreign affairs, information on the international environment in the form of foreign intelligence is communicated to the foreign policy decision-makers—ultimately, in the United States, the President. The challenges of the environment are met by policy decisions allocating resources of the state to effector elements of the executive branch for the achievement of national objectives by various techniques: diplomacy, foreign assistance, propaganda, military action, and so forth.

If we apply the concepts of sensitivity and stability to political systems we see distinct analogies even at an elementary level. The founding fathers of the United States wanted the legislature (decision-maker) sensitive to public opinion, so they introduced a House of Representatives elected biennially on the basis of population. But they did not want the decision process too sensitive to public opinion, so they introduced a Senate elected on a different basis for a different term of office whose concurrence is necessary to legislation. In order to introduce further stability into the system they decoupled the legislative (decision-maker) from the executive (effector) branch and introduced an independent control element in the form of a Supreme Court. The inherent stability of the system has been proved over the past 175 years. It is interesting to note that most of the proposals for "reform" recommended by political scientists are directed at increasing the sensitivity of the system to public opinion.

Each entity in our experience, whether physical object or person or social group, exists in time and interrelates with others in time. In the temporal order what will occur cannot provide a real input into antecedent action—but as a foreseen possibility it may provide an imputed information input. If we conceive of the current state of a system as determined by its antecedent states, the future states of that system are a set of probabilities dependent on the possible future states of its environments, and for self-regulating systems upon their actions in the "now." Insofar as the self-regulating system can know not only its actual state and the state of its environment in the "now," but can project and "know" alternative trajectories that are possible as realizable in the future, to this extent the future can be an input into decisional processes. While recognizing and attempting to predict the future states of key variables over which there is no effective control, individual and social planning consists essentially in: (a) projecting alternative trajectories as functions of direct action by the system and of the indirect effects of action by the system on its environment; and in (b) choosing the set of actions which, on the basis of past experience or subjectively assigned probabilities, seems most likely to bring about a future state conceived of as desirable. It is perfectly clear that the actions undertaken to achieve a future state of the system may *determine* to a considerable degree that future state. Hence it follows that in the reality of human affairs means and ends can never be separated.

Social systems not only respond to an existing environmental challenge, but they may foresee such challenges and plan to forestall them or cope with them in the future. In brief men and societies are provident—they respond not only to perceptions of reality but to the extrapolation of reality into possible future states. Much social choice depends upon the image of the future deemed desirable by a society and it is for this reason that the abstract ideology or the utopia expressed in concrete terms plays a critical role in defining social purpose and hence in conditioning social decisions. The range of possible response to an existing challenge is normally quite limited, while the range of autonomous action becomes increasingly broad as increasingly long future time-spans are anticipated. As given future goals become increasingly clear, that is concretely defined, social behavior may increasingly resemble that of a servomechanism in which guidance is reduced to control ". . . by the margin of error at which the object stands at a given time with reference to a relatively specific goal." Action may then become a routine problem of technical administration.

Action upon the environment is regulated by a continuing process of perception in which the perceived external reality is compared with an end state to be achieved. Now in this process it is clear that we are dealing with focused perceptions—that is a set of sensory inputs to which attention adverts selected from the innumerable alternative sets to which the person or group might advert. In an evolutionary sense only reasonably adequate criteria of perceptual relevance permit survival of a given biological species. For men whose criteria of perceptual relevation are largely cultural, only cultures having reasonably adequate criteria of relevance can survive. Similarly the norms of behavior of the person, the criterion values on the basis of which action is undertaken, are crucially important to behavior and to survival. These too are largely a matter of culture. In the history of mankind certain patterns of value have proved to possess a higher survival value than others. Within the range of viable systems of value and perceptual relevance (ideologies) there have been diverse degrees of success as measured by the extent of their diffusion and survival. In man we are dealing with a broad range of potential criteria of action and the possibility of self-conscious choice among sets of alternative criteria. Hence in dealing with social systems in which men form the ultimate self-regulating components, we must deal with the problem of the adequacy of perception and of value to effective action within a natural and human environment. The analysis of men and societies as self-regulating systems brings us back to the perennial philosophic problems of the Good and the True.

MAN-MACHINE SYSTEMS

Let us now conceive of the individual's environmental system in terms of a man-machine relationship. The machine is essentially a projection of the personality, normally subject to direct or indirect human control, capable of converting a given input or set of inputs into an output or set of outputs having greater imputed utility.

In its simplest form this is the man-tool relation in which the person serves as both a source of energy and of control. In more sophisticated man-machine systems prime movers may provide energy and man the control. At a more advanced stage the machine is in whole or part self-regulating and human control is exercised only in the programming phase. As we move to "learning machines" the human control interface may be reduced to the direct or indirect construction of the machine (indirect construction might involve programming a machine to produce a machine) and the direct or indirect programming of the criterion values on the basis of which decisions affecting output will be made. There is also a man-machine interface at the output since, presumably, the machine serves some human value. The most sophisticated man-machine systems today are basically extenders of human perceptive, data processing, and motor capabilities.

In some sense complex organizations, especially economic organizations, are man-machine systems in which the components are both men and artifacts in programmed interaction to convert input values into output values having a higher (ascribed) value. Within such an organization both persons and things are subject to decisions and the output values may or may not directly serve the human component of the system itself.

As we move from the realm of machines controlling machines, to men controlling machines, and to men controlling men in society we subtly shift the meaning of the term "control." In machine controls the message either actuates some multiplying device such as a relay or by combining with energic inputs modifies their characteristics. In human control of a machine, the person observes directly, or indirectly through an instrument display, the comportment of the machine in its environment and manipulates control devices. Here man-machine "interface" basically consists of displays and controls. Social control is the capacity (often based on control of material or financial resources) to manipulate the internal and/or external environments of other persons or groups so as to achieve a preconceived end. This normally involves selected changes in their information inputs designed to change in some way their perceptions or values so that they respond in the desired manner. It is largely concerned with "evoking" an "autonomous" response. Even the social effectiveness of negative sanctions in controlling behavior is contingent upon their being perceived and then evaluated more negatively than noncompliance. Basically, when dealing with objects as complex and autonomous as persons, control is reduced to presenting a challenge so structured that it evokes the desired response. Since social action normally involves a feedback loop, the socially controlled in some sense also control the controller; indeed this is the major characteristic of political decision-making in a democracy. Greniewsky points out: ". . . all control is communication. But on the other hand all communication is control. . . ."[19]

SYSTEM INTERFACES

A system interacts with its environment at the system boundary. Inputs move into the system across this boundary. Outputs move across this boundary into the system's environment. The area of contact between one system and another is termed an "interface." Operationally systems, and subsystems within systems, may be identified by the transactional processes that occur across their boundaries. For social groupings these transactional processes may involve the transfer of energy, material objects, men, money, and information.

The outputs of one social system are normally inputs for one or more other systems. These interrelations are amenable to analysis for economic sectors (and even for firms) by the use of input-output matrices. Quesnay in his *Tableau Economique* saw the national economy as an integrated system of monetary exchanges and exchanges of goods and services. The political system may be analyzed in terms of input demands and supports and an output of authoritative decisions that program the interrelations of persons and organized groups within the state. By extending our analysis to comprehend the five categories of exchange noted above, we are in a position to view the entire world as a (relatively) closed system of interrelated social components linked together by these transactional processes.

Communications and control technologies are already being extensively applied for purposes of social organization within the more advanced countries. The Soviet economy is now being organized on the basis of very extensive input-output matrices and computer programs designed to optimize resource utilization. These techniques may also help resolve the problem inherent in the limited use of market mechanisms to determine prices. By ascribing more or less arbitrary value to primary resource inputs (including the categories of human labor) all other prices in the economy can be made consistent. In the French indicative plan, a political decision, based on a consensus among all interested groups as to a future national mix of economic values, is reduced to an investment program that generates a high level of business confidence. The result has been an increasing tendency to reduce government to administration in terms of the technical achievement of concrete objectives. In the United States, the Social Security system has provided a means for national population control and is at the base of the new Internal Revenue Service computer system in which wage-earners and salaried persons are posted on a bi-weekly or monthly basis. Given the increasing use of electronic data processing in our banks, plus the sophistication and widespread use of credit facilities, it is quite conceivable that all monetary transactions over say twenty dollars could be posted in a national accounting system (at least aggregate) through the use of cascaded computers. This would, of course, largely do away with the possibility of robbery—but above all would provide a rapid running account of interregional and intersectoral exchanges that would permit the use of indirect controls at strategic points to effect very rapid adjustments of the economy in terms of programmed goals such as full employment and planned rates of economic growth. Such a system would also permit more equitable taxation by doing away with unrecorded transfers.

I would suggest that cybernetics today possesses great relevance for the social scientist. First it has begun to provide conceptual tools of the greatest importance for the analysis of complex systems and their interrelations. It establishes a focus on the critical importance of control and communications relations, of individual and institutional modes of perception and values. Certainly this view of men and societies as complex self-regulating systems, interacting among themselves within complex environments should prove conducive to a more holistic approach to the social and behavioral sciences in all their multivariate complexity, and provides us with a more solid foundation for systematic scientific formalization than existed in a past in which "science" *par excellence* comprised the simplified model of a clockwork universe governed by the laws of classical mechanics. Second, the social scientist must examine closely the actual and potential relations of cybernetic modes of thought and technologies to social institutions. Cybernetics has profound implications both as an ideology and as regards ideology. This is already abundantly clear in the works of both the Russians and the Anglo-Americans. Cybernetics technologies lie at the root of the quantum shift in economic relations called automation and cybernation. Computer based "optimum" decisions based on cost-effectiveness analysis have begun to replace the interplay of interest in some key areas of political decision–specifically in U. S. military spending. These techniques are potentially applicable to the whole budget process.

Certainly the political sphere will be a major forum for the resolution of the problems of value and social philosophy that can no longer be ignored. Even in the absence of sophisticated competitive economic and social systems and competitive concepts of a good life, such as those of Russia and France, these decisions could not long be postponed. What must now be demonstrated is the capacity of a democratic society to understand, confront, and resolve very complex problems of social organization in such a way as to retain traditional freedoms and consultative political institutions while moving into new patterns of economic and social relations in which we realize that our relation to the machine has become quasi symbiotic.

NOTES

1. Plato, *Republic,* I, 346 B.

2. A. M. Ampere, *Essay on the Philosophy of Science* (1838).

3. J. C. Maxwell, *Proceedings of the Royal Society* (London: 1868), XVI, 270–83.

4. Josiah Macy Foundation Conference on Cerebral Inhibition, May, 1942. A Rosenblueth, N. Wiener, and J. Bigelow, "Behavior, Purpose and Teleology," *Philos. Sci.,* X (1943), 18–24.

5. G. T. Guilbaud, *What is Cybernetics* (New York: Grove Press, 1960), p. 11.

6. H. Nyquist, "Certain Factors Affecting Telegraph Speed," *Bell System Technical J.* (April, 1924), 324; "Certain Topics in Telegraph Transmission Theory," *A.I.E.E. Transactions,* 47 (April, 1928), 617; R. V. L. Hartley, "Transmission of Information," *Bell System Technical J.* (July, 1928), 535.

7. C. E. Shannon and W. Weaver, *The Mathematical Theory of Communication* (Urbana: University of Illinois Press, 1949).

8. Y. Bar-Hillel, "An Examination of Information Theory," *Philos. Sci.,* 22 (1955).

9. N. A. Bershteyn, "New Lines of Development in Physiology and Their Relation to Cybernetics," *Problems of Philosophy,* 1962, 8, 78–87 (*JPRS,* 17, 117).

10. "Biological Aspects of Cybernetics," Moscow, 1962 (*JPRS,* 19, 637, p. 17).

11. *Ibid.,* p. 19.

12. N. Wiener, *God and Golem, Inc.* (Cambridge, Mass.: M.I.T. Press, 1964), p. 88.

13. *Encyclopedia of Science and Technology* (New York: McGraw-Hill, 1960): "Cybernetics: the science of

control and communication in all of its various manifestations in machines, animals, and organizations." ". . . an interdisciplinary science."

14. J. Bigelow, Address at Founders' Dinner, American Society for Cybernetics, October 16, 1964, Washington, D.C.

15. C. Babbage, *On the Economy of Machinery and Manufactures* (London: 1832). For a very recent application of advanced analytic techniques to management see S. Beer, *Cybernetics and Management* (New York: Wiley, 1959); "Toward the Cybernetic Factory," in Von Foerster and Zopf eds., *Principles of Self-Organization* (New York: Pergamon, 1962), p. 25.

16. L. Von Bertalanffy, "General Systems Theory," *General Systems,* I (1956); "General Systems Theory: A Critical Review," *General Systems,* VII (1962); J. G. Miller, "Toward a General Theory for the Behavioral Sciences," *Amer. Psychol.,* X (1955).

17. See K. Deutsch, *The Nerves of Government* (New York: The Free Press, 1963), p. 258; C. Dechert, "A Pluralistic World Order," *Proceedings* of the American Catholic Philosophical Association, 1963, pp. 167–186.

18. See D. Easton, "An Approach to the Analysis of Political Systems," *World Politics,* IX (1957), 383–400; R. Dahl, *Modern Political Analysis* (Englewood Cliffs: Prentice-Hall, 1963).

19. H. Greniewsky, *Cybernetics without Mathematics* (New York: Pergamon Press, 1960), p. 52.

CYBERNETICS AND THE PROBLEMS OF SOCIAL REORGANIZATION

Robert Theobald

I DO NOT INTEND TO MAKE AN INVENTORY OF the identifiable or predictable effects of computer technology and cybernation on our social institutions and then present these as the whole picture of the socioeconomic changes being brought about by the applications of cybernetics. For in addition to these kinds of specific and identifiable changes, there are already occurring other, fundamental changes in the socioeconomic system as a whole. These are being brought about through the drives exerted on the whole social fabric by the applications of cybernetics in the form of computerized systems.

Before discussing these drives we must look at the present state of computer application and its potential development. For some the computer seems the basis of all good, for others, the root of all evil. In these two allegorical roles, as a means of communication, and in a number of other functions, the computer is usurping the place of money. This fact is little understood, even by the informed public.

Computer manufacturers, like computers, increasingly talk among themselves. There is, therefore, a growing gap between the technological realities and public understanding of the potential of the computer and the speed at which developments are occurring.

Speaking before the 1964 Joint Fall Computer Conference, David Sarnoff, Chairman of the Board of the Radio Corporation of America, one of the country's leading computer hardware and software producers, outlined the way in which a universally compatible computer symbol-system will emerge and the unifying and systematizing effect it will have. Implicit in Sarnoff's remarks is the startling revelation that computer systems, not men, will first realize humanity's age-old dream of a universal language, and that the subtleties and nuances of human thought will risk being mediated through the restricted and standardized symbols of computer communication.

> We function today in a technological Tower of Babel. There are, by conservative count, more than 1,000 programming languages. And there are languages within languages—in one instance, 26 dialects, and in another, 35 dialects. There

are eight computer word lengths in use. There are hundreds of character codes in being, at a ratio of one code for every two machines marketed. Four magnetic tape sizes are employed with at least 50 different tape tracks and codes. Standards have not been accepted even for commonly used symbols, instruction vocabulary, or program development procedures. . . .
. . . The interests of the industry and the needs of the user demand a far greater measure of compatibility and standardization among the competing makes of computers and the means by which they receive and transmit information.

Tomorrow's standard computers and their peripheral equipment will instantly recognize a handwritten note, a design or drawing which they will store and instantly retrieve in original form.

The computer of the future will respond to commands from human voices in different languages and with different vocal inflections.

Its vocabulary will extend to thousands of basic words in the language of its country of residence, and machines will automatically translate the speech of one country into the spoken words of another. . . .

The interlocking world of information toward which our technology leads us is now coming closer to realization. It will be possible eventually for any individual sitting in his office, laboratory or home to query a computer on any available subject and within seconds to receive an answer—by voice response, in hard copy, or

> photographic reproduction, or on a large display screen. . . .
>
> This emerging pattern inevitably will set in motion forces of change within the social order, extending far beyond the present of presently predictable applications of the computer. It will affect man's way of thinking, his means of education, his relationships to his physical and social environment, and it will alter ways of living.

FUNDAMENTAL SOCIOECONOMIC EFFECTS OF COMPUTER APPLICATIONS

The computer ". . . will affect man's way of thinking, his means of education, his relationships to his physical and social environment, and it will alter ways of living." This dramatic truth, so clearly set out by Sarnoff, can be expressed even more briefly. We are passing out of the industrial age into the cybernetics era.

No attempt to list the implications of the shift from the industrial age to the cybernetics era can possibly be complete. Up to the present time, we have tended to examine what the introduction of cybernetics can do to and for certain fields: education, medicine, law, police-work, production, sales, administration, etc. While I will touch on many of these fields, I will be concerned primarily with the implications of the theory and practice of cybernetics on the total socioeconomic system.

My chief concern, as a social economist, is to examine the drives which arise from the development of cybernetics and to see how they can be employed to meet our fundamental goals—rather than subvert them. I am not interested in trying to use cybernetics to preserve our existing socio-economic system. Indeed, I intend to prove that continuation of this system will, in fact, make it impossible to realize our fundamental goals. Put another way, the recruiting of cybernetics to aid in the maintenance of some of our industrial-age values will make it increasingly difficult to realize these more basic goals.

I shall concentrate on four fundamental drives that arise from the application of cybernetics in the form of computer systems: the drive toward unlimited destructive power, the drive toward unlimited productive power, the drive to eliminate the human mind from repetitive activities, and the inherent organizational drive of the computer within a cybernetics system. I shall first examine the components of these drives; I shall then indicate the end results of these drives if we fail to change the present socioeconomic system; and finally, I will set out some of the minimum steps required to enable us to use these drives to achieve our fundamental goals.

Let me take up each of these four drives in turn. First, there is a drive toward unlimited destructive power. This results from the combination of nuclear energy with the control and communication system of the computer plus the activities of those involved in research and development. It is now generally accepted that there are already sufficient nuclear explosives, as well as bacteriological and chemical weapons, available to destroy civilization, if not all life.

Second, there is a drive toward unlimited productive power. This also results from the combination of effectively unlimited energy with the control and communication system of the computer plus the activities of those involved in research and development. While this drive toward unlimited productive power is still denied by the conventional economist, it is fully accepted by those most closely associated with production—the manufacturers and the farmer. American firms now expand their production, both within America and abroad, just as fast as they are able to increase profitable sales. There is no longer any effective limit to our productive abilities. We have passed beyond the dismal science of traditional economics. U Thant, Secretary General of the United Nations, has expressed this reality in the following words: "The truth, the central stupendous truth, about developed countries today is that they can have—in anything but the shortest run—the kind and scale of resources they decide to have. . . . It is no longer resources that limit decisions. It is the decision that makes the resources. This is the fundamental revolutionary change—perhaps the most revolutionary mankind has ever known." This is the true meaning of abundance: not that goods and services are already available and waiting to be used, but that we possess the technological potential to call forth enough goods and services to meet our needs.

Third, there is a drive to eliminate the human mind from repetitive activities. This results from the fact that the computer is a far more efficient drudge than the human being. We know that the production worker can be replaced by the cybernated system, that the computer controls inventory more effectively than the manager, that the computer handles bank accounts far more cheaply than the clerk. These, however, are primitive developments: in the near future we will see that the computer can take over *any* structured task: that is to say, any task where the decision-making rules can be set out in advance. Thus, for example, the computer will take over the process of granting most types of bank loan, the analysis of stock portfolios and the process of odd-lot trading on Wall Street. The last application is perhaps particularly noteworthy, for it will replace a group of people whose median income is around $50,000 a year.

The computer will force man's mind out of the repetitive productive system just as surely as industrial machinery forced out man's muscle. Gerard Piel, publisher of the *Scientific American,* has stated this truth in the following words:

> The new development in our technology is the replacement of the human nervous system by automatic controls and by the computer that ultimately integrates the functions of the auto-

matic control units at each point in the production process. The human muscle began to be disengaged from the productive process at least a hundred years ago. Now the human nervous system is being disengaged.

Fourth, there is an inherent organizational drive of the computer within a cybernetic system. The initial setting up of computer systems responds to a need to increase economic efficiency or to rationalize operations. But as computer systems become fully operative, a drive emerges toward the reorganization, for purposes of compatability, of interacting systems and institutions. The greater the number of areas of computer application, the greater the force behind this drive. There is now quite clearly a trend toward the emergence of a total computer system organized for maximum efficiency in terms of the coordination of large numbers of specific tasks.

Changes resulting from these four drives have already begun. The transformations taking place around us should not be regarded as the occurrences of random, isolated, nonpredictable events, but rather should be urgently studied to determine developing trends. We must always keep in mind the anthropological insight on culture change: that change brought about in one part of the system will be accompanied by other changes, both predictable and unpredictable, in many parts of the existing socioeconomic system and the entire culture.

It is now clear that the impact of the computer is destroying the industrial-age balance between the economy and the society. We continue, however, to assume that after a period of apparent disorganization, a new, favorable socioeconomic balance will become evident. We have further assumed that if it becomes clear that a satisfactory balance is not emerging, we will be able to intervene at the last moment to correct unfavorable trends. These kinds of assumptions would appear analagous to the economic theories of *laissez-faire* and, later, of precrisis intervention in the economy. But these theories were based on the impossibility of prediction and resulted in the establishment of a policy of remedial, not preventive, action.

Today, the availability of the computer enables us to spot trends long before they would otherwise be visible, to carry out the necessary discussion and to develop policies before the need for action develops. We can thus use these computers to control their own effects. Using information provided by computer systems, we can speed up the observation/discussion/action process so that we can keep up with the developments in our own technology. We can recruit technological drives to aid us in our effort to achieve our fundamental goals. Already information obtained through the use of computers can enable us to perceive rapidly both problems and opportunities. I will now try briefly to outline these problems and these opportunities and the kinds of society that would evolve from our failure or success in taking timely action in response to information already available. I will first discuss the developments that will inevitably follow if we fail to control our driving technology.

The fact that there are now sufficient nuclear explosives available to destroy civilization, if not all life, is now regarded almost as a cliché. New depth and meaning were, however, recently given to this realization in an article published in the *Scientific American* by Herbert York and Jerome Wiesner, both of whom have held high office in recent administrations. They stated: "The clearly predictable course of the arms race is a steady downward spiral into oblivion." The existence of the drive toward unlimited destructive power therefore condemns each country to undermine its own security in the very process of pursuing it.

Let us now turn to the problem posed by the drive toward unlimited productive power. So long as we preserve our present socioeconomic system, internal economic stability is *only* possible if the amount people and institutions are willing and able to buy rises as fast as the amount that we are able to produce. It is necessary that effective demand keep up with potential supply. The viability of our present scarcity socioeconomic system is based on a very simple relationship. It is assumed that it is possible for the overwhelming proportion of those seeking jobs to find them and that the income received from these jobs will enable the job-holder to act as an adequate consumer. The successful functioning of the present socioeconomic system is therefore completely dependent on an ability to provide enough jobs to go round. A continuing failure to achieve this invalidates our present mechanism for income distribution, which operates only so long as scarcity persists. So long as the present socioeconomic system is not changed, abundance is a cancer, and the various parts of the system must continue to do their best to inhibit its growth.

It is for this reason that business firms of all sizes, economists of almost all persuasions, and politicians of all parties agree that it is necessary to keep effective demand growing as fast as potential supply: that those who are still able to act as adequate consumers, because they are still obtaining sufficient incomes from their jobs, be encouraged to consume more and more of the kind of products that the economic system is presently organized to produce. Our economy is dependent on "compulsive consumption" in the words of Professor Gomberg, and manufacturers spend ever increasing sums on consumer seduction to persuade the consumer that he "needs" an ever wider variety of products.

Each of us has his favorite story about the evils of advertising. But a new dimension is being added to the diabolic in advertising by means of new techniques using programmed computers and automatic equipment; for example, a system has already been developed and is presently in use, at least on the West Coast and in Washington, where in a given neighborhood every phone will ring and a tape-recorded sales message will be played when the phone is picked up. The implications for quiet and privacy are too obvious to require comment.

Pressures from the attempt to keep supply and demand in balance are not limited to the mere constant irritative pressure to be aware of sales messages. There is a second type of consequence that is even more serious, for it acts to prevent any effective control of the drive toward unlimited productive power. Economist Paul A. Samuelson has expressed the new reality in the following extreme terms: "In the superaffluent society, where nothing is any longer useful, the greatest threat in the world comes from anything which undermines our addiction to expenditures on things that are useless." It is for this reason that it is difficult to close down obsolete military bases, to limit cigarette consumption, in fact to slow down any form of activity which might in any way create demand or jobs. In these conditions, the need for ever-higher demand will almost inevitably have priority over the needs described by the social worker, the sociologist and the philosopher.

Whatever we do, we can only succeed in delaying the inevitable: the attempt to keep demand growing as fast as supply and thus create enough conventional jobs will inevitably fail. The effects of the computer in developing abundance and eliminating jobs will inevitably exceed our capacity to create jobs.

And even while we continue our effort to maintain the present socioeconomic system, the situation will deteriorate. We will see a continuation of the trends of the past years during which the position of the unskilled and the uneducated has worsened, the plight of the poor has become ever more hopeless. Professor Charles Killingsworth, one of the leading experts on unemployment statistics, has shown that in 1950 the unemployment rate for the least educated group was four times the rate for the most-educated group; by 1962, the "real" rate for the bottom group was 12 times the rate for the top group. In a parallel development, the percentage of income received by the poorest 20% of the population has fallen from 4.9% to 4.7%. It should also be noted that during the five-year period ending in 1962, the income of high school graduates as compared with college graduates dropped from 60% to 52%.

Continuation of *present* trends is leading to a new type of organization of the socioeconomic system within which incomes and work time would be proportional. Starting at the bottom of the scale, there would be a large number of totally unemployed workers subsisting inadequately on resources derived from government schemes merely designed to ensure survival. The greatest proportion of the population would work considerably shorter hours than at present and receive wages and salaries that would provide for necessities and even some conveniences, but would not encourage them to develop a meaningful pattern of activity. A small number of people with the highest levels of education and training would work excessively long hours for very high salaries.

The effects of the drive toward unlimited productive power will, of course, not only be internal but will also affect the prospects of the poor countries. It is now clear that the gap between the rich and the poor countries is continuing to widen and that there is no possible way to reverse this trend until we change the existing socioeconomic system. It is shocking to realize that we have now reached the point where the *annual per capita increase in income* in the United States is equal to the *total income per capita* in some of the poor countries.

The reasons for this disparity are illustrated by the following two quotations. First, from the United Nations Development Decade report: "Taken as a group, the rate of progress of the underdeveloped countries measured by income per capita has been painfully slow, more of the order of 1 percent per annum than 2 percent. Most indications of social progress show similar slow and spotty improvement." And from a statement discussing the situation in India by B. R. Shenoy, director of the School of Social Sciences at Gujerat University: "Per capita consumption of food grains averaged 15.8 ounces per day in 1958, below the usual jail ration of 16 ounces, the army ration of 19 ounces and the current economic plan's target of 18 ounces. Since then, the average has fluctuated downward. Between 1956 and 1960, the annual per capita use of cloth fell from 14.7 metres to 13.9 metres."

The expressed policy of the Western powers is to aid the poor countries to catch up to the rich within an acceptable period of time. It has been generally argued, most explicitly in W. W. Rostow's *Stages of Economic Growth,* that the way the poor countries can attain this goal is to heed the lessons of history, to pass through the Western stages of growth, although hopefully at a faster pace. It is surely time we recognized the inapplicability of this policy.

The rate of economic growth of most poor countries now depends primarily on their being able to export enough goods to pay for their needed imports. It is clear that the poor countries will not be able to increase exports at an adequate rate to pay for the required growth in imports and that they will not be able to attain any reasonable rate of growth. The vast majority of the poor countries have no prospect of achieving an adequate standard of living so long as the present socioeconomic system continues.

Let us now turn to the prospect of freeing the mind of man from involvement in the repetitive productive process. There are a few optimists who persist in arguing that Western man can benefit immediately from the decrease in toil promised by the computer. An analysis of this conclusion suggests that those reaching it have not yet understood that it is typically those people whose life and educational experience ensure that they have the least adequate preparation for imaginative and constructive activities who will receive the largest increase in time not allocated to carrying out conventional jobs. This group is composed of two main categories: those with totally inadequate educations—the "poverty-cycle group," and those whose education and training have been slanted almost entirely toward conformity in order to enable them to perform tasks that will no longer be needed by the socioeconomic system.

Within our social economy a large number of individuals are already manifesting psychopathic symptoms as a response to loss of their roles in the system. Many economic analysts ignore the profound threat which the machines pose to deep-seated individual values and motivations. This threat is not manifest in economic statistics nor even in sociological monographs discussing the "world view" of the poor, but it is already affecting most members of society, both employed and unemployed. It is as all-pervasive as advertising, and, like it, it is constantly exerting pressures upon the individual, whether he be conscious of them or not. Some comments by psychiatrist Jack Weinberg illuminate this issue:

> Complicated machines which perform in intricate and invisible patterns are frightening. They are beyond the common man's understanding and he cannot identify with them. He

> experiences hostility toward such a machine, as he does toward most things he fails to understand. Furthermore, automation has done something that is unthinkable to a man who values his own self and that which he produces. In a sense, it has removed him from the product which he creates. . . . Work—no matter how odious an implication it may have to a person—is an enormously prized and meaningful experience to man. It is not all punishment for his transgressions as implied biblically, but it is also a blessing, not only for common-sense, economic reasons . . . but also because of its varied and unifying psychological implications.

Psychiatrists in clinical practice report increasingly that their patients are concerned because they feel that they function in an inferior way compared to machines, that their limbs are not acting as efficient machine-parts. They also report fantasies, such as dreams in which the patient is being backed into a corner by a computer. The popular arts—cartoons, comedy routines, and folk-songs—increasingly reflect these fears and influences of advanced technology and, above all, of the computer.

A. R. Martin, chairman of the American Psychiatric Association Committee on Leisure Time and Its Use, has summarized this problem in the following terms in a discussion of the role of medicine in formulating future public health policy:

> Symptoms of individual maladaption are: excessive guilt, compulsive behavior (especially

> compulsive work), increase of anxiety, depression, psychosomatic symptoms and suicide. . . . We must face the fact that a great majority of our people are not emotionally and psychologically ready for free time. This results in unhealthy adaptations which find expression in a wide range of sociopathologic and psychopathologic states. Among the social symptoms of this maladaption to free time are: low morale, civilian unrest, subversiveness and rebellion.

We are all aware of the manifest acceleration of past trends which bears out Martin's statement: let me briefly recall a few of them:

The crime rate is presently rising at about 10% a year as compared with a population increase of less than 2% a year.

Drug addition grows not only in the ghettoes but in the well-to-do suburbs, and young people are especially vulnerable to the activities of those who seek new recruits to the army of addicts.

America, as a society, tolerates over 40,000 deaths in automobile accidents a year, despite the fact that techniques of accident reduction are available for use.

There is a fascination with violence. This was dramatically illustrated by a recent event in New York when 40 interested spectators remained indifferent to the appeals of an 18-year-old bruised and bloodied office worker as she tried to escape from a rapist. Similarly in Albany, a crowd gathered to urge a mentally disturbed youth to jump to his death. Two comments reported in *The New York Times* are hardly believable: "I wish he'd do it and get it over with. If he doesn't hurry up we're going to miss our last bus." And another: "I hope he jumps on this side. We couldn't see if he jumped over there."

The problem of increased violence and crime was raised in the recent presidential campaign, but a meaningful discussion never developed. The growing extent of the problem was underlined by the police chief of Los Angeles, William H. Parker, in a question and answer interview in *U.S. News and World Report* in April 1964:

> *Question:* Has the crime picture changed much in [the last 37 years?]
>
> *Answer:* Not only has the crime picture changed, but the entire attitude of the American people toward crime, I think, has undergone quite a definite change. I think there is a tendency to accept crime as part of the American scene, and to tolerate it. . . .
>
> *Question:* America might have the choice, eventually between a criminal state and a police state.
>
> *Answer:* I believe that will become the option before us if crime becomes so troublesome that we are no longer able to control it.

I have been discussing societal and psychological deterioration primarily with reference to the removal of the human mind from repetitive productive activity as a result of the installation of computer systems. To many it will appear that I have overstated my case in casting the computer in the role of the root of all evil. I would therefore like to emphasize that my point here is only that it *can* be just that in the future, for it can accelerate existing disfunctional socioeconomic trends.

It is true that these societally disfunctional trends began long before the computer appeared on the socioeconomic scene, but it is also true that our attempts to reverse these trends will be frustrated if we continue to regard the ability of the computer to act with maximum efficiency in carrying out an immediate task as more important than all of our fundamental values put together. As long as we regard these values as of minor importance, to be upheld only when it is convenient to do so, we will be unable to recruit the computer to help us to attain our fundamental goals.

Whether increasing violence and social disorder can fairly be laid at the door of the computer is, however, peripheral to the possibility of the development of a police state. The only question is whether we will become convinced that our predominant need is for greater control over the individual and the means we will use to achieve it.

We have so far failed to perceive that the types of control made possible by the inherent organizational drive of the computer within a cybernetic system have no common measure with our past experience in organization. The generalized use of the computer as a means of societal control threatens to destroy at least the privacy, and very probably *all* the present rights, of the individual unless we change the socioeconomic system. Let us be very clear: the only way to run the complex society of the second half of the twentieth century is to use the computer. The question is to determine the rights of the individual under these circumstances and then to ensure that they are respected by the computer-using authorities.

The danger is imminent. Government already holds very substantial dossiers on a major part of the population. These are either in computer memories or can be placed in computer memories. Information on the financial affairs of each individual will soon be available through the development of the Internal Revenue Service Computer System. It is now planned that the records of the Job Corps will be placed on computers, a step which will inevitably be extended to cover *all* those that the government considers to be in need of help to find or regain a place in society. In the area of the exercise of socially sanctioned force and compulsion, it is significant that New York State is developing a statewide police information network: a network which all authorities agree could be extended nationwide within a brief period of years.

It is no longer possible to dismiss such works as *Brave New World* and *1984* as mere literary nightmares. I do not believe that I exaggerate when I say that almost all those who have looked not simply at one, but rather at all four of the drives

I have discussed, agree that some form of dehumanized, impersonal world is inevitable in the next 20 years unless we make major changes in our socioeconomic system. In particular, I remember very clearly the comment of one individual very heavily involved in the development of new computer applications, who said to me that the only thing wrong with the descriptions of the internal police state in *1984* was that the date was at least 10 years too late.

Unless we consciously develop new policies, we will destroy all the goals we have striven so long to achieve. Only the working out of a new socioeconomic balance with the aid of society's servants—computer systems—will enable us to meet our fundamental societal goals.

I have been discussing the effect of the drives exerted by the application of computers in reinforcing certain industrial-age values and thus inhibiting our forward movement into the cybernated era. I will now turn to a consideration of the potential of these drives as aids in the effort to move toward the realization of our fundamental societal goals in the new context of a cybernetics-based socioeconomy. It is my contention that the positive potential of these drives will not become a reality as long as we continue to subordinate efforts to correct socioeconomic ills to the goal of the continuation of an outmoded industrial-age system, with its now inappropriate set of restraints and freedoms. If we are to have a more fulfilling way of life in the cybernetics-based abundance era, we must take conscious steps to enable us to arrive at a new set of restraints and freedoms and a new balance between them.

I will attempt to indicate briefly some of the steps which I consider to be of first importance. Those who are interested in a fuller discussion of these and related subjects will find more detailed descriptions in my books *The Rich and the Poor, The Challenge of Abundance,* and *Free Men and Free Markets.*

Let us begin with a consideration of the drive toward unlimited destructive power. It is now generally accepted that this can only be prevented from destroying mankind if we renounce force, and that this requires that negotiation and arbitration become the means of settling disputes. In effect, nations will have to move toward world cooperation and world law. We are, at the present time, witnessing the early efforts of institutions which could become the creators and administrators of world law, but we continue to view such efforts as primarily aimed at peace-keeping. Our perception of the role of world cooperation in achieving socioeconomic advances remains very dim, for we still allow language and cultural barriers to impede the free flow of information. The physical barriers to communication are being lifted. New channels are opening. Our role is to insure that we use them, not allow ourselves to be persuaded that we should block them once again.

The drive toward unlimited productive power

can result in vast benefits, both internationally and domestically, but only if we change the methods presently used to distribute rights to resources. It is, of course, impossible to determine the final pattern that will emerge, but I believe that the need for three steps can already be seen.

1. The rich countries should accept an unlimited commitment to provide the poor countries of the world with all the resources they can effectively employ to help them to move into the cybernetics-based abundance era. Let me state explicitly, however, that such a commitment should not be accompanied by the right to dump unwanted surplus industrial-age products and machinery into the poor countries. Rather, the poor countries must move as directly as possible from the argicultural era to the cybernetics era, without being forced to pass through the industrial-age process of sociocultural and economic realignments.

Domestically, we should adopt the concept of an absolute constitutional right to an income through provision of basic economic security. This would guarantee to every citizen of the United States, and to every person who has resided within the United States for a period of five consecutive years, the right to an income from the federal government sufficient to enable him to live with dignity. No government agency, judicial body, or other organization whatsoever should have the power to suspend or limit any payments assured by these guarantees.

2. A second principle, committed spending, should also be introduced. This would embody the concept of the need to protect the existing middle-income group against abrupt and major declines in their standard of living, for a very substantial proportion of this group will lose their jobs in the next decade. This principle is based on the premise that in the process of transition between the industrial age and the cybernetics-based abundance era, socioeconomic dislocation should be avoided wherever possible, whether caused by sudden large-scale reduction in demand or by sudden withdrawal of economic supports for valid individual and social goals.

Let me remind you that the validity of the classic objection—"we cannot afford it"—has been destroyed by the drive toward unlimited productive power. We can afford to provide the individual with funds that will encourage and enable him to choose his own activities and thus increase his freedom, and, *at the same time,* increase, to the required extent, expenditures on community needs: particularly education, medical services, housing, recreation facilities, and conservation.

3. There is now general agreement that if we are to profit from the drive to eliminate the human mind from repetitive tasks we must greatly increase our emphasis on education. We have been unwilling to face up to the fact that the school and the university were designed to serve the requirements of the industrial age. We have therefore concen-

trated our attention on longer periods of education for more and more people, rather than on changing the educational system to make it appropriate for the cybernetics era.

An attempt to lengthen the time spent in school and college will not be enough. We must find ways to develop the creativity and to enlarge the capacity of each individual in terms of his own uniqueness. We will have to teach people to think for themselves, rather than to absorb and then regurgitate with maximum efficiency the theories of past thinkers. I believe the best way to do this is to change our educational process from being discipline-oriented to being problem-oriented: to set up educational systems which will force people to face all the implications of each problem and to evaluate the individual's potential in terms of his ability to perceive new interconnections between aspects of the problem.

We must do this in such a way as to avoid the "new education" emphasis on means, the smoothly interacting group or seminar, and concentrate on ends, the kind of problems that will be studied. I think this can probably best be achieved through what we can call the two-dimensional seminar technique. Here the choice is up to the individual; he enters the systems at the first level with a multiple choice of seminars; he can then go on to specialize by movement up the levels of complexity in one problem area or he can choose to gain wider knowledge by horizontal movement, through participation in many seminars.

Education along problem-oriented lines is the prime necessity of the future and it is also the prime reason why we cannot preserve our present industrial-age values nor return to the simple values of the agricultural era. The set of values of the cybernetic era will be unique; attitudes toward time and space, production and consumption, will have to be appropriate to the realities of this era. In the future we are going to value those who can take a systems approach in all fields—not only about the problems of society but also about the individual. For example, the patient will respect his doctor on the basis of his ability to understand him as a biological system rather than value his seeming quasi-magical techniques as in our agricultural past.

I am sure that many humanists will be shocked by my acceptance of systems-thinking, for they fear that man will be destroyed by the rationality implicit in it. In this view the rational is synonymous with the logical solution to any problems inherent in a task, the choice of the one best way to do something, the constant search for the efficient. Compared to any system or smoothly running organization, man's thought processes are less rational, more subject to accident and distortion. According to this thesis, it follows that man must inevitably end by acting according to the instruction of the efficient decision-making mechanisms which he himself created for his service, to carry out his wishes, to fulfil his needs. But the efficient, knowledgeable servant becomes the administrator and thus the master. This is the case put forward by Jacques Ellul in his book originally published in France in 1952 under the title of *La Technique,* and recently published in the United States under the title *The Technological Society.* It is impossible not to concede the immense strength of Ellul's argument, even though it was based on the organizational efficiency drives existing before the emergence of the computer and its accelerating drive toward maximum efficiency.

Up to the present time, automation, which should be described as advanced industrial mechanization *not* involving the use of computer systems, has been predominant in industrial reorganization. Automation sets up a few inherent drives for system-linkage. As cybernation—the combination of advanced machinery with the computer—develops on the factory floor and as cybernetic systems develop within organizations, the drive toward linking of systems will grow rapidly stronger. Cybernation has its *own inherent* drives which demand the linkage of systems. This was the prime fact made clear in Sarnoff's recognition that the absence of a single computer language is now the major impediment to large-scale systems link-up and that the efforts of the computer industry must be directed to rapid elimination of this barrier.

My acceptance of systems-thinking is based on reality: on my willingness to face up to the fact that there is no way to avoid the development of large-scale computerized systems in the second half of the twentieth century. Our only hope is to accept this reality and to use all of man's energy to recruit technological drives for the attainment of our fundamental goals.

The increasing efficiency of organization permits greater output with less energy input. In the industrial scarcity age, this process worked to our advantage because demand exceeded supply and energy sources were always insufficient. In the cybernetics-based abundance era, however, we are being confronted with the need to place restraints on both production and on new energy sources, lest their drives destroy us. The danger of exploding production is no less real than that of destructive explosions. It is incorrect to assume that because presently we have unfulfilled global production needs, we can absorb any extra amount, and rapidly.

We are living in a world of exponential growth. But Dennis Gabòr, professor at the Imperial College of Science and Technology in London, has pointed out: ". . . exponential curves grow to infinity only in mathematics. In the physical world they either turn round and saturate, or they break down catastrophically. It is our duty as thinking men to do our best toward a gentle saturation, instead of sustaining the exponential growth, though this faces us with very unfamiliar and distasteful problems."

For many people the most distasteful of all these problems is the fact that there is already insufficient toil to go round—that it is now necessary to allow vast numbers of people to do what *they want to do* simply because they personally believe that their activity is important. The guaranteed income proposal mentioned above recognizes this reality, and it has therefore been attacked from both ends of the political spectrum, and from every point in between, on the grounds that the proposal would promote the lazy society. For example, August Heckscher, who served as President Kennedy's special assistant for cultural affairs, declared: "The very idea of large populations doing nothing but pleasing themselves goes against the American grain," and then went on to make proposals for job allocations and income distribution which Gerard Piel has described as "instant feudalism."

We have not yet been willing to recognize the true extent of the challenge posed by the drive toward unlimited destructive power, unlimited productive power, the elimination of the human mind from repetitive tasks, the organizing drive of the computer within a cybernetiated system. We have not yet been willing to recognize that we live today in the truly lazy society—a society where we allow technological trends to make our decisions for us because we have no mechanisms to allow us to control them. We have not yet been willing to recognize that man's power is now so great that the minimum requirement for the survival of the human race is individual responsibility.

Man will no longer need to toil: he must find

a new role in the cybernetics era which must emerge from a new goal of self-fulfillment. He can no longer view himself as a superanimal at the center of the physical universe, nor as a super-efficient taker of decisions self-fashioned in the model of the computer. He must now view him-self as a truly creative being in the image of a creative God.

COMPUTERS AS TOOLS AND AS METAPHORS

Ulric Neisser

BY NOW IT IS A COMMONPLACE THAT CYBERnetics and automation will bring about radical changes in our way of life. Indeed, our purpose is to see how these changes can be predicted and understood, and thus brought under control for desirable ends.

The computer brings about change in two ways. There is no doubt that the new technology has given us a powerful kit of tools. They are bound to be used; we must determine who is to use them and to what ends. In this respect our problem is like that posed by other new tools. Atomic energy is a case in point. Many conferences have been convened to consider both the opportunities and the dangers of the nucleus: what kind of reactors should be built, who should control them, how their dangers might be minimized. A similar technological approach to the promises and perils of cybernetics is both possible and desirable. I will make a specific suggestion along these lines a little later.

Before considering the computing machines' potential as a tool, I would like to think of it in an entirely different role. It serves us not only as an instrument, but as a metaphor: as a way of conceptualizing man and society. The notions that the brain is like a computer, that man is like a machine, that society is like a feedback system, all reflect the impacts of cybernetics on our idea of human nature. This metaphoric status of the computer is closely bound up with its use as a tool. The goals we set out to achieve and the society we want to make depend on our idea of what men are really like.

The notion that man is like a machine is by no means new. As an analogy it has been with us literally for ages. It has always been in competition with other analogies: that man is like an animal, or like an angel, or like a devil. Indeed, there are some respects in which man does resemble even the simple machines with which previous centuries were familiar. To see the likeness and the difference let us analyze the classical idea of a machine.

First of all, a machine in the old-fashioned sense is something material, something tangible, made of parts like wheels and levers. All of its actions follow from the same principles that govern the behavior of other physical objects. This implies that its behavior is comprehensible in terms of these principles; we can understand it. If it is perhaps too large or complicated to be understood in its entirety, at least it is "piecewise comprehensible": we know what the parts do, and it is natural to believe that nothing fundamentally new is added by conjoining them. From this follows the notion that a machine must be predictable: it can do nothing that will surprise us, since we know just how it works. If it surprises us nevertheless, we can conclude that it is breaking down.

In addition, the classical notion of a machine includes both activity and a kind of passivity. Machines are active. They move and make an impression on their environment. Nevertheless, their motions are in direct response to the commands of their operator. The airplane that flies from Boston to Washington today will fly back tomorrow if the pilot wants to; it will not suddenly insist on seeing Disneyland instead. Nor will it adapt to changed conditions and fly a different route by itself if the weather is bad.

Finally, of course, the idea of a machine implies that someone constructed it. A man put it together out of unrelated parts. A duplicate could be constructed again, if anyone were so minded. No machine can be unique. In summary, a machine has been thought of as something that obeys physical laws in a comprehensible way, that carries out predictable actions at the whim of an operator without making autonomous demands or novel adaptations, and that was constructed once and could be constructed again.

The analogy between men and such machines as these was based on materialism. Men are also physical objects; they are made of the same substances as are other things and presumably could be comprehended in terms of physical laws if only we knew them all. But however marked these similarities were thought to be, the differences between men and machines were even more compelling: men are not predictable, their behavior is both autonomous and adaptive, they are not constructed from parts, and they cannot be duplicated. So, ordinary men did not take the metaphor of the machine seriously, although it provided fuel for philosophical debate.

Recently, two factors have entered to change the situation. On the one hand, devices have been built that (so it is said) are more like men than the old machines were. Modern computers can be programmed to act unpredictably and adaptively in complex situations. That is, they are intelligent. On the other hand, men have behaved in ways that (so it is said) correspond rather well to our old ideas about mechanisms. They can be manipulated, "brain-washed," and apparently controlled without limit. With this sharp increase in the number of properties that men and machines seem to have in common, the analogy between them becomes more compelling. The remaining differences tend to be washed away. Maybe men could be constructed too; do we not hear of artificial limbs, artificial kidneys, artificial hearts? Maybe men's uniqueness and their residual autonomy are illusions; television has accustomed us to illusions of life.

As a result of these trends, the last few years have witnessed an obsessional concern with the notion of man-the-machine. The frequency with which this idea is represented in comic books, television, movies, and science fiction is so great that a Jungian might well accord it the status of an "archetype." An archetype is a classical figure or image that plays an important part in fantasy. The good mother, the bold hero, and the evil tempter are all archetypes, and they appear as clearly in contemporary media as in the most ancient legends. The same kind of evidence now suggests the existence of an archetype of the mechanical man. Its most explicit representations are as "living dolls," zombies, and robots, but it also appears in stories about persons who lose their human identities as a result of "brain-washing" or hypnosis.

Coupled with the popularity of robot fantasies has come extraordinary willingness to believe in the manipulability of men. Not only the advertising agencies and their customers, but also their critics are willing to credit "Madison Avenue" with demonic powers. The available evidence suggets that no such powers exist. Persuasion is a tricky business, which fails oftener than it succeeds. It must be remembered that an advertising campaign that influences 2% of the prospective market is a great commercial success and that a high proportion of all promotions are failures. Such terrifying devices as "subliminal advertising" turn out to have subliminal effects. Even high-pressure political campaigns change few minds. But demonstrations of the *in*effectiveness of manipulation are widely ignored. The notion that men are machine-like has taken deep roots, and being partially unconscious it is partially invulnerable to evidence.

The rising credibility of the machine metaphor has serious consequences, both within and outside the context of our discussion here. It is important for us, because it may alter the purposes the new technology is to serve. If men are basically similar to the computers they operate, if society is a cybernetic system closely analogous to the mechanical devices it employs, an optimal social design has has one shape; if they are very different, it has another.

Apart from considerations of social planning, "mechanomorphism" can be seen to have a direct effect on the cultural climate. Although men may be tempted to think of themselves as automatons, they do not like it. Fascinated as they may be with the thought of being manipulated, they also resent it. Such a characterization denies them freedom and dignity. Freedom presupposes autonomy, and dignity assumes uniqueness. To refute the allegation that they are only machines, many people—especially adolescents, for whom personal dignity is particularly important—will go to almost any lengths. The apparently senseless violence and destructiveness reported daily in the newspapers can be seen, in part, as an attempt to demonstrate autonomy and uniqueness. The vandal and the murderer may be the worst kinds of men, but no one thinks of *them* as machines. To all who will listen, their actions say, "See, I cannot be manipulated; I cannot be understood; I cannot be successfully imitated; there is no one like me." Crime has always been symbolic of freedom.

The metaphor of man-the-machine has dangerous implications, as long as it remains an unconscious determinant of behavior. The *New Yorker* magazine, which delights in the vagaries of the English language, occasionally prints a choice item under the caption "Block that Metaphor!" (I particularly cherish one which read, "The Fascist octopus has sung its swan song.") Can we block the machine metaphor? One positive step is a relatively careful analysis of the manipulability of men, along the lines suggested above. Another step is an analysis of the capacities and limitations of today's computer programs.

We must begin by admitting that machines can behave intelligently and purposively. Such a direct use of these terms may be surprising. Is not a machine something made of simple and unintelligent pieces? Indeed it is, but here as elsewhere the whole is more than the sum of its parts. Out of many thousands of simple operations by relays or transistors can come something unpredictable and adaptive, perhaps a new proof for a logical theorem or persistent search for an elusive target.

Let us consider an example. In a program written by Gelernter, a computer can be set to seek the proof of a theorem in geometry, the same sort of problem that might give a bright high school student considerable food for thought and cause a less gifted one to give up entirely. The computer (or perhaps one should say, the program) will begin by trying some simple rules of thumb. Should these fail, the computer will formulate some conjecture that would advance the solution if it could be proven true. Having made such a conjecture, the computer will check its plausibility in terms of an internal diagram of the situation. If the conjecture is plausible, its proof is sought by the same rules of thumb as before. Once proved, the conjecture will serve as a steppingstone to the desired theorem. If the conjecture is rejected as implausible or unprovable, others will be tried along promising lines until one has succeeded or the computer's resources are exhausted. Not even the programmer knows in advance whether the machine will succeed in proving any given theorem. The number of steps involved is so great that their endpoint cannot be predicted.

I would not deny that the computer has behaved intelligently. Avoiding blind trial and error, it has selected and pursued promising hypotheses. Moreover, its strategy is similar to the procedure a good high school student might use. But does it really act as he would? There are some interesting differences. When the theorem has been proved, the geometry program will be erased from central storage. Another program, perhaps one for mechanically translating German into English, can easily be substituted. The computer will then begin translating, with the same single-mindedness and efficiency with which it formerly sought proofs. (Actually it will be somewhat less successful, because translation turns out, surprisingly, to be harder than proof-finding.) Superficially, this change of behavior is much like that of the student. He can be seen to leave geometry class when the bell rings and to go next door to study German. Despite this resemblance, a real difference exists.

The student's mental activity is not as easily controlled, or observed, as is his location. He may well continue (consciously or unconsciously) working on the proof when he should be doing German. Whether he does so or not, neither the teacher nor the student himself can undo the previous hour's experiences. On the other hand, he may never have given much thought to either subject. Throughout both classes, he may have been musing about last night's dance, or tomorrow's football game. Adolescence is not an age at which he can give undivided attention to geometry or any other academic discipline; he has more important things to do.

The description I have just given embodies two psychological axioms. I have described the student as a person, an ego, with a continuing sense of his own history and identity. And in saying that the student had "more important things to do," I have assumed that persons grow through a series of stages and focal concerns in an order that does not yield easily to outside pressure. Their central storage cannot be erased, nor can it be loaded with arbitrary programs. These assumptions about human nature deserve some discussion.

Many psychologists have tried to describe the course of human development. Freud has surely been the most influential, and in certain respects his formulation of growth has never been seriously challenged. For example, hardly anyone doubts that the focus of sensual pleasure in the normal child begins in the oral regions and gradually shifts elsewhere. Perhaps these shifts are irrelevant to our discussion, but I doubt it. During the same period the child's accumulating experience, slowly forms his ego and his sense of self. He comes to know who he is, what he has been, and what his capacities are, both in relation to the inanimate world and to other people. These changes are largely irreversible, because they involve the process of learning as well as its product. The new concepts serve to channel and interpret still further experiences. He soon feels unique, special, as if there were no one like him, because the concept he has of himself is very different from his concept of anyone else. This conviction of uniqueness is not only inevitable but (to some extent) objectively correct. There *is* no one like him. No one has had just his particular history, and so no one else can see things just as he does. And he cannot help but become still more different from everyone else as he grows older; now even those events that he shares with others will be interpreted and assimilated by him in ways that are purely his own.

Recently, other psychologists, most notably Erikson and Piaget, have expanded the Freudian developmental scheme. Erikson has extended it longitudinally, finding regularities in human development far beyond the kindergarten age. For example, he distinguishes the concern for how things work and for acquiring effective skills that characterize the prepubertal child from the crucial search for identity, for a self of which one can be proud, which comes in adolescence.

I have presented this brief potpourri of developmental psychology to emphasize several objective characteristics of real people that make the machine metaphor inappropriate. Each person *is* unique, because he is the irreversible product of a very particular history. No man can be manipulated without limit, nor can anything once done to a person be entirely undone, as a machine can be cleared and reset. Psychological development follows certain crude but definite lines that are determined by the nature of the organism. Any attempt at social planning which neglects these considerations is in for substantial surprises.

I do not mean, of course, that it is *logically* impossible to write a program that would imitate cognitive development. "Logical" demonstrations of irreducible differences between men and machines will always fail. What I do assert is that we have no such programs now and that we have no skills which lead me to expect any in the near future.

In the course of development, each man acquires a sense of autonomy and a sense of self. These are not simply experiences; they also become needs. Although they are by no means the only motives we have, they are real enough. A. H. Maslow has pointed out that human needs are arranged in a kind of crude hierarchy. It is only when we have attained at least tolerable relief from hunger that we search for security; only when we are at least somewhat secure that we can give and receive love. The need to be free, to make responsible decisions about one's own life, is certainly not at the base of the hierarchy. It is a truism that starving men are not much concerned about their liberties. Yet the need to be independent is always ready to play its part when circumstances permit. It arises as the inevitable consequence of normal human development. Every child experiences autonomy and uniqueness; the exercise of autonomy results in a special kind of satisfaction attainable in no other way.

Unfortunately, the sense of freedom is perishable. It is lost when men must spend all their energy in the service of more basic needs, but also if they stop believing in their freedom, if they think of themselves as impotent and manipulated, or if they believe that they are little better than machines. But in addition to these dangers, which we have already considered, there is another. Freedom may be lost in a more obvious way, common enough in history. Men may be adequately fed and self-confident besides, and still be unable to make choices because their environment does not permit it. As a psychologist, I have so far dwelt on the dangers to autonomy that come from within. We must not overlook the danger of regimentation and control from without, by force of social convention. If I do not elaborate on them here, it is because the perils of both dictatorship and conformity are already quite well known.

Curiously, this threat of being controlled against one's will, and under protest is often *also* represented mythologically by a machine. Our vocabulary is full of phrases like "totalitarian machine," "the wheels of progress," "Communist Party apparatus," and "just a cog in the machine." Charlie Chaplin brought the archetype to life in the film "Modern Times." Here the machine does not stand for a kind of diminished man but for a force beyond the control of its victim. To be sure, other metaphors—storms, tides, and fate—are also available to describe irresistible forces. But there is a special poignancy in picturing someone crushed by a machine; the machine was built and so presumably might have been built otherwise. If Chaplin's nemesis had been more thoughtfully constructed (or not constructed at all), it wouldn't have caught him. His entrapment was unnecessary. At the very least, somebody could have turned the thing off.

As a metaphor, this second use of the machine is as incomplete as the first. Societies are as unmechanical as men, and for similar reasons. They have their own dynamics, their own laws of growth, and their own integrity. What we are caught in is no mechanism. At least it has no switch with which it can be disconnected. But I will not press the point; these are questions for a sociologist. No matter how society is conceptualized, it is objectively true that men can be boxed in by social patterns which leave little or no meaningful autonomy. This loss of freedom can result in the same kind of desperate and destructive behavior that I have already described. Indeed, the two kinds of unfreedom are hard to disentangle; coercion from without easily becomes coercion from within.

It appears, then, that man enters the cybernetic age at a considerable disadvantage. It *will* be an age of intelligent machines; they *will* control some aspects of our lives. How can we use these devices constructively when we are so ready to fear them?

Such a question is part of the technological problem. Machines are tools, to be used by men. Men, unlike current or foreseeable machines, are unique and autonomous, with a corresponding need to exercise autonomy. They also have a long-standing belief that machines threaten their freedom. Given such conditions, how should our tools be shaped? Is it possible for machines to preserve and extend man's sense of integrity instead of threatening it?

I believe that it is indeed possible, though far from inevitable. Before arguing this question directly, I must make a short digression. I invite you to consider a remarkable and much maligned machine, with which most of you have a good deal of experience. It has rather a bad reputation among intellectuals and public officials. Nevertheless, it continues to be a never-ending source of pleasure for millions of people and a mainstay of the economy in the bargain. I refer to the common (or clover-leaf variety) automobile.

Cars are nothing but machines, but no one will deny their important influence in our lives. Their existence has transformed society, and by no means just for the better. Indeed, many observers regard the automobile as a menace. Auto accidents are a major cause of death; the landscape is eroded by spreading highways; the air is polluted by exhaust fumes; the cities are choked with traffic. Do I dare put in a good word for such a blight? Notice that these disadvantages, impressive as they may be, are physical, not psychological. The evidence shows overwhelmingly that people *like* cars. Every rational plan for what is called "public transportation"—trains, subways, and buses—has had to deal with a deep-rooted preference for doing one's own driving. Given half a chance, most people would rather go where they like, when they like, under their own control.

Whatever its defects, the automobile is one machine that extends our sense of autonomy instead of shrinking it. In conscious and unconscious fantasy, it usually plays a part very different from the other mechanical archetypes we have been considering. Cars are symbols of freedom, autonomous movement, sex, individual prestige, and social mobility. In a mythical sense, the man with a car is driving the machine age rather than being driven by it. If we can endow the information-processing devices of tomorrow with a similar character, cybernetics will increase rather than limit our sense of freedom.

Is it possible to have any feeling of personal control over a computer? One would not think so at first. Contemporary machines carry out more symbol manipulations in a second than man can in a year; they store more information than does any encyclopedia, and refer to it in microseconds. And indeed, the traditional mode of dealing with computers makes it very clear who is boss. The machine's input must be very carefully prepared, with religious attention to detail, usually by punching holes in *just* the right places on pieces of *just* the right cardboard. Before he can even punch the cards, the user must learn secret and cumbersome languages with cabalistic names—"Fortran," "Algol," "IPL-V." When he has done his part, he must wait for hours or days, while the machine dispassionately serves all comers. Eventually it deigns to give him some return. If he has misplaced so much as a single comma in his offering, he will get back gibberish or nothing at all. When something useful finally appears, after many attempts, it consists of literally reams of paper and literally thousands of numbers. The user can then look forward to long hours of decoding and abstracting before he has the answer to his question.

The computers which make these demands on their users certainly contribute to the Chaplinesque stereotype of the machine. Ponderous and inflexible, they demand and get compliant behavior from the men around them. If, in addition, they display a mysterious kind of intelligence, that seems all the more cause for our alarm. But do they have to be so demanding?

If the computer has great capacities for translation, why must it be the *user* who struggles to translate his language into cabalistic symbols? If computers can carry out their tasks in fractions of a second, why must their users wait hours or days to discover an error in programming? How can a device of such speed and flexibility seem slow and inflexible? Why does an instrument susceptible of such precise and detailed control seem so uncontrollable?

In fact, none of these disadvantages follows from

any principle of cybernetics. They are only the initial state of the art of automatic computation. Convenient control over so powerful a device requires rather sophisticated techniques. The necessary techniques include both "hardware" and "software"—that is, both electronic gadgetry and the right kind of programs. Quite naturally, these were not developed until computers themselves already existed. So for the first decade of the computer age, we have been in the position of a man who has the Library of Congress at his disposal but has not yet invented the card catalogue.

In short, computers seem remote, demanding, and inflexible only because we have not set our minds to making them accessible, responsive, and adaptable to our needs. This situation is rapidly changing. Several computer installations across the country are experimenting with systems that radically change the "balance of power" between the machine and its users. In these systems, the computer is instantly available, and one can use it without leaving one's office. Instructions can be given in languages more or less like English, on the keys of an ordinary electric typewriter. If the machine cannot interpret the instructions, it types back a request for clarification. The desired computation is carried out as soon as the instructions are clear. The results appear on the same typewriter, in any format the user may request. In some systems the computer can also present diagrams and graphs on conveniently located television screens. There are even installations in which the user himself can draw on the surface of a screen to express his wishes to the computer pictorially.

In summer, 1964 I had the privilege of working at one such pioneering installation, Project MAC (machine-aided cognition) at M.I.T. The project is making an accessible computer of this kind available to scientists and engineers in the expectation that their work will be substantially aided. The letters also stand for the "multiple-access computer," which is MAC's basic instrument. A single central computer is connected by telephone cables to more than a hundred separate terminals, many of which are located in the laboratories, offices, and homes of the users. The terminals are electric typewriters or teletypes. (One terminal is also equipped with a cathode-ray tube to permit the television-like intercommunication I mentioned before; more are planned.) In principle, any user may turn on his typewriter and set to work at any time, no matter how many others are already doing so. The machine switches its attention rapidly from one terminal to another and can usually service all of them within a second or two. Thus each user feels as if he had complete, instantaneous control of the full machine. (In practice, this ideal situation is not quite reached. Traffic jams and delays do occur, but they need not concern us here.)

The user can give his instructions in any of a wide variety of computer languages and has many specialized programs available that may suit his specific needs. If he is a physicist, a program for the computation he wants may well be stored in the computer's files already. A few typed instructions and a little input data yield a result that would have taken two days to get under the old system, and two years without a computer. If he is a linguist, he finds a computer language specially designed to handle verbal material and translation programs. If he is a civil engineer, he can describe a proposed structure and its materials in a special language designed for his purposes and be told immediately where the strong and weak points of the structure are. He responds by typing back changes in the structure this information suggests to him; in return he receives new information on the effect of his changes.

In 1964 the system was as yet unfinished, but even so we found most users were enthusiastic. In those fields where MAC has been used most successfully, research problems are being solved ten times as fast as before, and tasks are being undertaken that would otherwise have seemed insuperable. Moreover, using MAC is fun. The user is in control. He knows what is happening and makes it happen when and how he likes.

At MIT in the summer of 1964, I interviewed more than 60 of its users. All had what might be called a "healthy" attitude toward the computer. None of them personified it; none of them feared it; for none did it play the archetypical role of the dangerous machine. To be sure, many were angry at one or another feature of the system, and many —if not most—were occasionally frustrated by it. But their negative reactions seemed natural and appropriate. They reminded me of the way one may feel about one's car. A car can be a nuisance; it may break down, require too much attention, get caught in traffic jams, and so on. Nevertheless, we would not readily give up the freedom and flexibility it provides.

At this point, you may feel that I have given an overspecialized answer to a very general problem. Perhaps you are willing to grant that scientists and engineers can experience an increased sense of mastery and accomplishment in the use of such a system. But scientists and engineers are not the bulk of the population, nor will they ever be. It would seem that ordinary people, at least, will only continue to feel oppressed by machines that have more and more human skills while they become less and less comprehensible.

To argue in this way is to misunderstand the potential of the new technology. The very word "computer" is misleading; computation is only one function of digital machine and need not be the most important. To wonder what nontechnical people would do with an approachable computer is like wondering, a few hundred years ago, what they would do with pencil and paper. They will use it for reference: whole libraries will be available in anyone's home at the touch of a finger. They will use it for their own records, for correspondence, for travel information, for tax computations, for game-playing, for artistic composition, for control of household machinery. Perhaps most crucially, they will use it for education, at home and at school, and at all stages of life. I foresee a time when computer terminals will be as widely distributed as television sets are now, at the same order of expense, when students will use them to do their homework in every field—from history and Latin to information technology—and adults will interrogate them to find out where the trout fishing is likely to be good or whether Goldwater really said that in 1964.

If such a time ever comes, it will bring its own problems and demand its own readjustments, as have the automobile and the television set. But I am sure that at such a time the computer will not be surrounded by the air of dangerous mystery which veils it now. One will not think of machines as uncontrollable forces if one controls them every day for one's own purposes. One will not think of human beings as manipulable robots when one has discovered that robots are indeed manipulable whereas one's wife remains stubborn. Moreover, as private individuals have access to a greater share of the new technology's resources, they will become in fact less manipulable, less susceptible to false claims, more able to judge matters for themselves.

Knowledge is power. The approaching age of cybernetics gives us the opportunity to disseminate this kind of power as widely as electricity is disseminated today. If we do so, men will become more autonomous, more unique, and less like machines than they have ever been.

CYBERNATION AND CULTURE

Marshall McLuhan

TODAY YOUNG PEOPLE ARE IN THE HABIT OF saying, "Humor is not cool." The old-fashioned joke with its story line has given way to the conundrum: e.g., "What is purple and hums?" Answer: "An electric grape." "Why does it hum?" "Because it doesn't know the words!" This kind of joke is involving. It requires the participation of the hearer. The old-fashioned joke, on the other hand, permitted us to be detached, and to laugh *at* things. The new kind of joke is a gestalt or configuration in the style of set theory. The old-fashioned story is a narrative with a point of view. This helps to explain a strange aspect of humor raised by Steve Allen.

In his book *The Funny Men,* Steve Allen suggests that "the funny man is a man with a grievance." In Canada at present the Quebec separatists are a people with a grievance. A whole stock of stories has come into existence in connection with their grievances. For example, there is the story of the mouse that was being chased by the cat. The mouse finally discovered a spot under the floor to hide in. After a while it heard a strange "Arf! Arf! Bow! Wow!" sort of sound and realized that the house dog must have come along and chased the cat away. So the mouse popped up, and the cat grabbed it. As the cat chewed it down, the cat said, "You know, it pays to be bilingual!"

The story line as a means of organizing data has tended to disappear in many of the arts. In poetry it ended with Rimbaud. In painting it ended with abstract art, and in the movie it ends with Bergman and Fellini. One way of describing our situation in the electronic age is to say that we have come to the end of the Neolithic Age. The Neolithic Age brought in, thousands of years ago, a new pattern of work and organization. It represented a transition from the age of the nomadic hunter and the food-gatherer to the age of the sedentary and agrarian man. The Neolithic time began with the specializing of human work and action that gave us our great handicrafts, including script and writing, whether on stone or papyrus. Not until script, around 3000 B.C., did man begin the first enclosures of space that we call architecture. There is no architecture known in any culture earlier than script. The reasons for this are very instructive. Man's orientation to space before writing is nonspecialist. His caves are scooped-out space. His wigwams are wrap-around, or proprioceptive space, not too distant from the Volkswagen and the space capsule! The igloo and the pueblo hut are not enclosed space; they are plastically modelled forms of space, very close to sculpture.

Sculpture itself, which today is manifesting such vigor and development, is a kind of spatial organization that deserves close attention. Sculpture does not enclose space. Neither is it contained in any space. Rather, it models or shapes space. It resonates. In his *Experiments in Hearing,* Georg Von Bekesy found it expedient to explain the nature of sound and of auditory space by appealing to the example of Persian wall painting. The world of the flat iconic image, he points out, is a much better guide to the world of sound than three-dimensional and pictorial art. The flat iconic forms of art have much in common with acoustic or resonating space. Pictorial three-dimensional art has little in common with acoustic space because it selects a single moment in the life of a form, whereas the flat iconic image gives an integral bounding line or contour that represents not one moment or one aspect of a form, but offers instead an inclusive integral pattern. This is a mysterious matter to highly visual and literate people who associate visual organization of experience with "the real world" and who say "seeing is believing." Yet this strange gap between the specialist, visual world and the integral, auditory world needs to be understood today above all, for it contains the key to an understanding of what automation and cybernetics imply.

To anticipate a bit, and to capsulate a good deal, let me suggest that cybernation has much in common with the acoustic world and very little in common with the visual world. If we speak in configurational terms, cybernation tends to restore the integral and inclusive patterns of work and learning that had characterized the age of the hunter and the food-gather but tended to fade with the rise of the Neolithic or specialist revolution in human work and activity. Paradoxically, the electronic age of cybernation is unifying and integrating, whereas the mechanical age had been fragmenting and dissociating.

Today, at the end of the Neolithic Age, we have the bomb as environment. The bomb is not a gimmick or a gadget. It is not something that has been inserted in the military establishment any more than automation is something that is now being inserted into the industrial establishment. The bomb, like automation, is a new environment consisting of a network of information and feedback loops. In moving from the mechanical to the electronic age, we move from the world of the wheel to the world of the circuit. And where the wheel was a fragmenting environment, the circuit is an integrating environmental process. The bomb, as pure information, consists of the higher learning.

It is, as it were, the extension division of the modern university in its highest research areas, creating, as it does, a very tight environment indeed.

The bomb takes over all earlier technology and organization. It also makes us vividly aware of all human cultures as responsive cybernetic systems. We are never made aware of our environment until it becomes the content of a new environment. The culture in which a man lives consists of structures based on ground rules of which we are mysteriously unconscious. (This is a matter that has been eloquently demonstrated in *The Silent Language* by Edward T. Hall.) But any change in the ground rules of a culture nonetheless modifies the total structure: and cybernation, far more than railway or aeroplane, speeds up information movement within a culture, effecting total change in perception and outlook and social organization.

In moving from the Neolithic Age to the electronic age, we move from the mode of the wheel to the mode of the circuit, from the lineal single plane organization of experience to the pattern of feedback and circuitry, *and* involvement. During the many centuries of specialist technology, man cultivated habits of detachment and indifference to the social consequences of his new specialist technologies. In the age of circuitry the consequences of any action occur at the same time as the action. Thus we now experience a growing need to build the very consequences of our programs into the original design and to put the consumer into the production process. By awakening to the significance of electronic feedback we have become intensely aware of the meaning and effects of our actions after centuries of comparative heedlessness and noninvolvement.

Another way of looking at our situation today in the age of cybernation and information machines is to say that from the time of the origin of script and wheel, men have been engaged in extending their bodies technologically. They have created instruments that simulated and exaggerated and fragmented our various physical powers for the exertion of force, for the recording of data, and for the speeding of action and association. With the advent of electromagnetism a totally new organic principle came into play. Electricity made possible the extension of the human nervous system as a new social environment. In 1844 Sören Kierkegaard published his *Concept of Dread*. This was the first year of the commercial telegraph, and Kierkegaard manifested clairvoyant awareness of its implications for man. The artist tends to be a man who is fully aware of the environmental. The artist has been called the "antennae" of the race. The artistic conscience is focused on the psychic and social implications of technology. The artist builds models of the new environments and new social lives that are the hidden potential of new technology.

In *Fortune* magazine, August, 1964, Tom Alexander wrote an article entitled "The Wild Birds

Find a Corporate Roost." The "Wild Birds" are science fiction writers retained by big business to invent new environments for new technology. Big business wants to know what kind of world it will have created for itself in ten years or so. That is to say, the big enterprises have become aware that their technological innovations tend to create new environments for enterprise and for bureaucracy. Yet these environments are almost imperceptible except to the artist. If, in fact, the businessman had perceptions trained to read the language of the arts, he would be able to foresee not 10, but 50 years ahead in all fields of education, government, and merchandising. It is one of the ironies of the electronic age that the businessman must become alert and highly trained in the world of the arts. It is one of the mysteries of cybernation that it is forever challenged by the need to simulate consciousness. In fact, it will be limited to simulating specialist activities of mind for some time to come. In the same way, our technologies have for thousands of years simulated not the body, but fragments thereof. It was in the city alone that the image of the human body as a unity became manifest.

In *Preface to Plato* Eric Havelock traces the changeover from tribal to civilized society. Before the environmental pervasiveness of writing occured in the fifth century B.C., Greece had educated its young by having them memorize the poets. It was an education dedicated to operational and prudential wisdom. It is sufficiently manifest in the

Odyssey of Homer. The hero of that poem, the wily Ulysses, is called *Polumetis,* the man of many devices. The poets provided endless practical illustrations of how to conduct oneself in the varied contingencies of daily life. This type of education Havelock very fittingly calls "the tribal encyclopedia." Those undergoing this type of education were expected to know all things whatever, in heaven or in earth. Moreover, they were expected to share this wisdom with all members of the tribe, much as educated English people today are expected to know *Alice in Wonderland.* It was, therefore, a considerable revelation when writing came to detribalize and to individualize man. In creating the detribalized individual, phonetic literacy created the need for a new educational program. Plato, says Havelock, was the first to tackle this problem directly. Plato came up with a spectacular strategy. Instead of the "tribal encyclopedia" he advocated classified data. Instead of corporate wisdom, he taught analytic procedures. Instead of the resonating tribal wisdom and energy, Plato proposed a visual order of "ideas" for learning and organization. The fascinating relevance of Havelock's book for us today is that we seem to be playing that Platonic tape backwards. Cybernation seems to be taking us out of the visual world of classified data back into the tribal world of integral patterns and corporate awareness. In the same way the electronic age seems to be abolishing the fragmented and specialist form of work called "jobs" and restoring us to the nonspecialized and highly involved form of human dedication called "roles." We seem to be moving from the age of specialism to the age of comprehensive involvement.

Since this is a very confusing and even terrifying reversal in human affairs, it may be helpful to take a second look at the general pattern of development. We may take some consolation from the anecdote of a clerk at a toy counter. When he saw a customer curiously scrutinizing one of the toys, he spoke up. He said, "Madam, I can recommend that toy. It will help your child to adjust to the modern world. You see, no matter how you put it together, it's wrong!"

In approaching the manner of significance of cybernation as an environment of information, it is helpful to consider the nature and function of other environments created by other extensions of the human organism. For example, clothing as an immediate extension of our skin serves the function of energy control and energy channel. An unclad population, even in a warm climate, eats 40% more than a clad population. Clothing serves, that is, as a conserver of energy for doing tasks that the unclad could not undertake. The unclad man in the jungle after 24 hours without food and water is in dire straits. The heavily clad Eskimo at 60 degrees below zero can go for days without food. Clothing, as a technology, is a store of energy. It enables man to specialize. The consequences of clothes in terms of changing sensory organization and perception are very far-reaching indeed.

One of the most fantastic examples of the consequences of seemingly minor technological change is described by Lynn White in *Medieval Technology and Social Change*. His first chapter concerns the stirrup, the extension of the foot. The stirrup was unknown to the Greeks and Romans, came into the early medieval world from the East. It enabled men to wear heavy armor on horseback. Men became tanks. It became mandatory to have this equipment; yet one suit of armor required the skilled labor of one man for an entire year. The landholding system did not permit small farmers to pay for such equipment. To finance the production of armor so necessary to the needs of social élites, it became expedient to reorganize the entire landholding system. The feudal system came into existence to pay for heavy armor. When the new technology of gunpowder appeared, it blew the armor right off the backs of the knights. Gunpowder changed the ground rules of the feudal system as drastically as the stirrup had changed the ground rules of the ancient economy. It was as democratic as print.

The extension of the nervous system in electronic technology is a revolution many times greater in magnitude than such petty extensions as sword, and pen, and wheel. The consequences will be accordingly greater. At the present time, one area in which we daily observe the confusion resulting from sudden change of environmental factors is that of the educational dropout. Today the ordinary child lives in an electronic environment. He lives in a world of information overload. From infancy he is confronted with the television image, with its braille-like texture and profoundly involving character. It is typical of our retrospective orientation and our inveterate habit of looking at the new through the spectacles of the old that we should imagine television to be an extension of our visual powers. It is much more an extension of the integrating sense of active touch. Any moment of television provides more data than could be recorded in a dozen pages of prose. The next moment provides more pages of prose. The children, so accustomed to a "Niagara of data" in their ordinary environments, are introduced to nineteenth-century classrooms and curricula, where data flow is not only small in quantity but fragmented in pattern. The subjects are unrelated. The environmental clash can nullify motivation in learning.

Dropouts are often the brightest people in the class. When asked what they would like to do, they often say, "I would like to teach." This really makes sense. They are saying that they would rather be involved in the creative processes of production than in the consumer processes of "sopping up" packaged data. Our classrooms and our curricula are still modelled on the old industrial environment. They have not come to terms with the electronic age and feedback. What is indicated for the new learning procedures is not the absorption of classified and fragmented data, but pattern recognition with all that that implies of grasping interrelationships. We are actually living out the paradox of having provided cities that are more potent teaching machines than our formal educational system. The environment itself has become richer. We seem to be approaching the age when we shall program the environment instead of the curriculum. This possibility was foreshadowed in the famous Hawthorne experiment.

Elton Mayo's group found at the Hawthorne plant that whether they varied working conditions in the direction of the agreeable or the disagreeable, more and better work was turned out. They concluded that observation and testing, that is an involved environment, as such, tended to change the entire work situation. They had discovered that the prepared environment for learning and work must be ideally programmed for new perception and discovery. The workers at the Hawthorne plant were not merely being observed. They were sharing in the process of discovery. The classroom and the curriculum of the future will have to have this built-in pattern of discovery in order to match the potential of improved information movement. The world of cybernation offers the immediate possibility of programming all education for discovery instead of for instruction and data input. This was the great discovery of Maria Montessori, who found that the prepared environment worked wonders far beyond the level of the prepared curriculum.

One of the misconceptions attending the onset of cybernation and automation is the fear of centralism. Indeed, on all hands automation is greeted as a further development of the mechanical age. In fact, automation abolishes the patterns and procedures of the mechanical age, though at first, like the horseless carriages with large buggy-whip holders, a new technology is set to perform the old tasks that are quite unsuited to it. Cybernation in effect means a new world of autonomy and decentralism in all human affairs. This appears obvious in so basic a matter as electric light and power, but also applies at all levels. For example, the effect of Telstar when it is fully operative will be to supplant the centralism of present broadcasting networks. Instead of extending a common pattern to a whole range of human affairs, the tendency of cybernation is toward the custom-built-in production and toward autonomy and depth in learning. It would be easy to illustrate these patterns of development from the world of poetry and painting and architecture in our time. My topic suggests that I should relate it to the world of ethics and religion. One need mention only the ecumenical movement or the liturgical movement of our time to get one's cultural bearings in these matters. Both of these movements have in common an emphasis on the pluralistic and stress on participation and involvement.

To many people these new patterns seem to

threaten the very structure of personal identity. For centuries we have been defining the nature of the self by separateness and nonparticipation, by exclusiveness rather than inclusiveness. It is true that the electronic age, by creating instant involvement of each of us in all people, has begun to repattern the very nature of identity. All the philosophers and artists of the past century have been at grips with this problem. But whereas before the problem of identity had been one of meagerness and poverty, it has now become the problem of abundance and superfluity. We are individually overwhelmed by corporate consciousness and by the inclusive experience of mankind both past and present. It would be a comic irony if men proved unable to cope with abundance and riches in both the economic and psychic order. It is not likely to happen. The most persistent habits of penury are bound to yield before the onslaught of largesse and abundant life.

A HUMANISTIC TECHNOLOGY

Hyman G. Rickover

BY BORING INTO THE SECRETS OF NATURE SCIentists have discovered keys that will unlock powerful forces which are then put to practical use by technology. The apparatus we have set up to utilize these forces is now so huge, so complex, so difficult for laymen to understand that by its very magnitude it threatens to dwarf man himself. The threat does not inhere in the apparatus itself; technology is neutral. It lies in ourselves, in the way we look at technology, for this determines what we do with it.

My plea is for a humanistic attitude toward technology. By this I mean that we recognize it as a product of human effort, a product serving no other purpose than to benefit man—man in general, not merely some men; man in the totality of his humanity, encompassing all his manifold interests and needs, not merely some one particular concern of his. Humanistically viewed, technology is not an end in itself but a means to an end. The end itself is determined by man.

Technology is nothing but tools, techniques, procedures—the artifacts fashioned by modern industrial man to increase his powers of mind and body. Marvelous as they are, we must not let ourselves be overawed by these artifacts. They certainly do not dictate how we should use them, nor by their mere existence do they authorize actions that were not anteriorly lawful. We alone must decide how technology is to be used and we alone are responsible for the consequences. In this as in all our actions we are bound by the principles that govern human behavior and human relations in our society.

This needs stressing for there is a widespread notion that, since technology has wrought vast changes in our lives, traditional concepts of ethics and morals are now obsolete. Why should the fact that technology makes it possible to relieve mankind of much brutal, exhausting physical labor and boring routine work affect precepts that have guided Western man for centuries? This may brand me as old-fashioned, but I have not yet found occasion to discard a single principle that was accepted in the America of my youth. Why should anyone feel in need of a new ethical code because he has become richer or healthier or has more leisure? Does it make sense to abandon rules one has lived by because one has acquired more efficient tools? Tools are for utilizing the *external* resources at our disposal; principles are for marshaling our *inner,* our human resources. With tools we can alter our physical environment; principles serve to order our personal life and our relations with others. The two have nothing to do wtih each other.

It disturbs me to be told that technology "demands" some action the speaker favors, or that "you can't stop progress." It troubles me that we are so easily pressured by purveyors of technology into permitting so-called "progress" to alter our lives, without attempting to control this development—as if technology were an irrepressible force of nature to which we must meekly submit. If we reflected we might discover that much that is hailed as progress contributes little or nothing to human happiness. Not everything new is *eo ipso* good, nor everything old out of date.

Perhaps what makes us receptive to these arguments is our tendency to confuse technology with science. Not only in popular thinking but even among well-informed persons, the two are not always clearly distinguished. Characteristics pertaining to science are often attributed to technology. The etymology of the word may have some bearing on this confusion. Its suffix lends to techno*logy* a false aura—as if it signified a body of accumulated, systematized knowledge, when in fact the term refers to the apparatus through which knowledge is put to practical use. The difference is important.

Science has to do with discovering the facts and true relationships among observable phenomena in nature, and with establishing theories that serve to organize masses of verified data concerning these facts and relationships. Julian Huxley said that scientific laws and concepts are "organized creations of the human mind, by means of which the disorderly raw material of natural phenomena presented to crude experience is worked into orderly and manageable forms."

Because of the extraordinary care with which scientists verify the facts supporting their theories, and the readiness with which they alter theories when new facts prove an old, established theory to be imperfect, science has immense authority. What the scientific community accepts as proven is not debatable; it must be accepted. No one argues that the earth *ought* to attract the moon or that atomic fission *ought not* to produce energy.

Technology cannot claim the authority of science. It is properly a subject of debate, not only by experts in the field but by the public as well. In every field of knowledge, application to human use of scientific theories and axioms has proved anything but infallibly beneficial; in fact much harm has been done. We have yet to devise methods for testing the safety and usefulness of a given technology that would in any way be comparable to the methods by which science tests its hypotheses.

The forces put to work by technology should be handled with greater care than they are presently. We have been remiss in failing to insist that no one be allowed to manage a technology who does not have the requisite competence. Further, we should insist that anyone making a faulty decision that causes damage to others be held responsible. As it is, many are now making technological decisions who are not capable—even if they would—to assess the consequences of their decisions. Too often these decisions are made on the basis of short-range, private interests with no regard for the interests of others or the possibilities of harmful long-range side effects. A certain ruthlessness is encouraged by the mistaken belief that to disregard human considerations is as necessary in technology as it is in science. The analogy is false.

The methods of science require rigorous exclusion of the human factor. They were developed to serve the needs of scientists whose sole interest is to comprehend the universe; to know the truth; to know it accurately and with certainty. The searcher for truth cannot pay attention to his own or other people's likes and dislikes or to popular ideas of the fitness of things. This is why science is the very antithesis of "humanistic," despite the fact that historically modern science developed out of and parallel to the humanism of the Renaissance.

What scientists discover may shock or anger people—as did Galileo's insistence that the earth circles the sun or Darwin's theory of evolution. But even an unpleasant truth is worth having; besides, one can always choose not to believe it! It is otherwise with technology. Science, being pure thought, harms no one; it need not therefore be humanistic. But technology is action and thus potentially dangerous. Unless it adapts itself to human interests, needs, values, and principles, that is, unless it is humanistic, technology will do more harm than good. For by enlarging man's power of mind and body, it enhances his ability to do harm even as it enhances his ability to do good. Never in all his long life on earth has man possessed such enormous power to injure fellow human beings and society. Neither public opinion nor the law have caught up with his new destructive potential. This is why perpetrators of technological damage often escape with impunity.

That a humanistic technology is within the bounds of the attainable is proved by medicine. The practicing physician's technology is permeated by the humanistic spirit; it is centered on man. No one is allowed to practice medicine who has not given proof of his technical competence. The profession operates under a code of ethics that requires physicians to place the human needs of patients above all other considerations. On graduation from medical school they swear an oath incorporating this ethical code—an oath formulated two and a half millennia ago by the Greek physician Hippocrates.

We owe to Greece the noble idea that knowledge ought to be used humanistically, instead of for personal aggrandizement or power, or as a means of extracting maximum gain from people who are in need of the services of men possessing special knowledge. It was a novel idea at the time, and remains unknown to this day in many regions of the world—witness the fear in which medicine men are commonly held because of their notorious abuses of power. Even among the people of Western civilization, the precept is rarely followed outside medicine and a few other professions. Most human affairs are conducted on the old Roman maxim of *caveat emptor*.

Pursuant to the Greek ideal, the tradition in Europe has been to restrict the practice of medicine to persons who not only are competent in their specialty but who are also broadly or humanistically educated. Hence the requirement that before they begin their medical studies future physicians must obtain the baccalaureate that comes at the end of the exacting course of a classical or semiclassical gymnasium or lycée—a course deemed to nurture better than any other those qualities of breadth of mind and depth of character that are prerequisites of a humanistic attitude.

This, of course, prolongs the time it takes to become a physician and increases the cost. During the past century it was widely felt in our country that this was "undemocratic." So young men were allowed to enter medical school directly from high school. But eventually we followed the example of Europe, realizing that if medicine is to be of greatest service to mankind it must be practiced as a humanistic profession. Since we have nothing in our public school system comparable to the humanistic gymnasium or lycée, we require that before being admitted to medical school students obtain a bachelor's degree from a liberal arts college—the nearest American equivalent to the European baccalaureate.

I should like to see a similar requirement set up by engineering schools. They are now, in most cases, mere trade schools, though often excellent in their narrow field. Even schools that find room in their crowded curriculum for humanities courses cannot make up for the deficiencies of the American high school. We have no alternative but to demand completion of a liberal arts college course if we want future professionals to be broadly and liberally educated before they specialize for their particular career.

I have long believed that engineering should be practiced as a humanistic profession, that engineers should be humanistically or liberally educated persons. This would bring us appreciably closer to a humanistic technology, not only because it would broaden the engineer's vision but also because it would raise his professional status. This is particularly important today when most engineers work in large bureaucratic organizations—private and public—where professional judgment has difficulty making itself felt against the autocratic fiat of higher administrative officials. If the technical advice of engineers is to count, they must attain a professional status comparable to that of physicians.

I speak of this with feeling. My work is in one of the new technologies, one that is dangerous unless properly handled. I am frequently faced with the difficulty of convincing administrative superiors that it is not safe for them to overrule their technical experts. Here is a case in point.

A superior once asked me to reduce radiation shielding in our nuclear submarines. He said the advantage of getting a lighter-weight reactor plant was worth risking the health of personnel. It was not possible to make him see that such a concept could not be accepted; that, moreover, where radiation is involved, we are dealing not just with the lives of persons today but with the genetic future of all mankind. His attitude was that we did not know much about evolution and if we raised radiation exposures we might find the resulting mutations to be beneficial—that mankind might "learn to live with radiation."

In a humanistic technology the desire to obtain maximum benefits is subordinated to the obligation not to injure human beings or society at large. Technological decisions must be made by competent and responsible persons who know that nature will strike back if her categorical imperatives are disregarded. We need for technology as a whole a system comparable to the one in medicine which guards against practices that, while doubtless profitable to the practitioner, would be harmful to those who suffer the consequences; in other words, we need professionalization of the decision-making process.

Most technological decisions are made by large organizations. Their custom of exalting the "pure" administrator above the technical expert, even in technical matters, needs to be changed. For in our country we do not make it mandatory that administrators have technical competence; their *metier* is to rule organizations. Living in hierarchies, they are accustomed to giving and obeying orders; they expect, and they give, unquestioned obedience to superiors. This offers little room for personal judgment based on knowledge and expertise. Professional persons, on the other hand, are trained to act in professional matters on their own judgment, no matter what their position in the organization. They also place the ethical code of their profession above the interests of their employer. We would be well advised to ponder whether we ought not insist on professionals participating on an equal basis in the decision-making process whenever a technology is potentially dangerous.

This brings me to a final and important question.

Can we handle technology in such a way that it will not distort our free society? Does our political system provide means to control the new power complexes that have arisen as a consequence of technology? Can we make certain that these do not diminish the autonomous individual on whom our system pivots, that they do not by reason of their overwhelming power pervert the democratic process?

This is so large a subject that I can only touch upon a few aspects that seem to me important. Let me say at once that if ours is to remain a society of free men, technology must be made humanistic. Men will not retain their liberty unless their society is totally committed to the Protagorean belief that "man is the measure of all things" and to Kant's maxim that "man is an end in himself" and must not be used "as a mere means for some external purpose."

In essence, what we face is a modern version of an age-old problem that keeps reappearing: *how to reconcile liberty and civilization.* We shall understand the present-day version better if we know something about the eighteenth-century version that occupied the thoughts of the Founding Fathers. They saw the problem and ultimately solved it brilliantly—for *their* time.

They were men of the Enlightenment—that last phase of the Renaissance when men turned once more for inspiration to the classical world as they mounted an attack on every custom and institution that shackles the mind of man or arbitrarily restrains his action—from superstition to class privilege, from tyranny by an established church to tyranny by an absolute monarch. The central problem agitating the thinkers of the Age of Reason was how to limit power so that men may be free. They saw more clearly than anyone before or since that it was civilization, life in civilized society, that created the problem. Savages knew how to remain free, but when men lived in civilized society their social needs generated power which in the end suppressed their liberties.

Though separated by the Atlantic from the center of all this intellectual ferment, the founders of our nation were a part of it. Unlike the European philosophers, who were merely theorizing about a possible resolution of the antithesis between individual liberty and organized society, the Founding Fathers were looking for a practical solution. They were first-rate thinkers, but also experienced politicians. Their great achievement was to have recognized that on this rich, empty, newly colonized American continent a new type of self-reliant man, a new type of basically egalitarian society had come into being, and that a unique opportunity thus offered itself to establish here the Utopia the philosophers were dreaming about: a country where all men would be free to manage their personal lives, where the law recognized no special privilege or handicap, where government would be the servant, not the master, of the people. With consummate skill they devised a political system combining maximum protection of individual liberty with adequate provision for the proper governance of a civilized society. Hamilton called the Constitution a happy mean between "the energy of government and the security of private rights."

The founders achieved their purpose by making consent of the people indispensable to the functioning of government, in other words, by associating the citizen with the business of governing. In an oversimplified way, one could say that the individual in our society is a person with private rights and public duties; he safeguards his private liberties by conscientiously attending to his public responsibilities.

The fundamental tenets of our political system are to be found in the Declaration of Independence, the machinery putting them into effect in the Constitution. Familiarity with these great documents and with the *Federalist,* which elucidates their meaning, is as essential to a strong democratic faith as is the Bible to religious faith. We must know them well enough to be able to distinguish clearly between tenet and technique, between principle and procedure. For to preserve our free society we have to adjust techniques and procedures to changes in the conditions of life in order that they may be kept effective, while holding on to the basic tenets of principles that make ours a free, democratic society.

The Declaration of Independence enumerates

three fundamental principles in the following order of precedence: first, men are born equally endowed with certain rights that are "inalienable"; second, governments are established to "secure" these rights; and third, government derives its "just powers" from the consent of the governed. Clearly the intent of the founders was that Americans were to be forever secure in the rights that make men free and, being free, capable of exercising control over their government; that never would they be ruled by anyone who had not received a public mandate and was not accountable to the people for his actions.

The founders were well aware that democracy is the most difficult form of government. They knew that to make a success of it, a people must have political sagacity as well as what the ancients called "public virtues"—a combination of independence, self-reliance, and readiness to assume civic responsibilities. But they felt that Americans possessed these qualities, that, indeed, the conditions of life in America developed just the type of man who would know how to make democracy work.

Among the advantages favoring a workable democracy, the founders counted the fact that Americans were for the most part independent farmers, artisans, and merchants. Being used to managing their own business, such men would, they felt, know how to manage the nation. A scarce population and the immense wealth of the country in land and other resources would prevent formation of a propertyless class dependent on others for employment. The political equality basic to our system of government would thus be firmly supported by real equality among our people. The founders were convinced that there would be free land for generations and generations to come. They could not have envisioned a hundredfold population increase in only two centuries. That 70% of our people now live in urban conglomerations would have horrified them. They judged Europe's propertyless urban masses unfit to govern themselves! To them America's unique advantages were a guarantee of success for their political experiment. They felt that the land, the people, and the political system were made for each other.

These special advantages are nearly all gone now. They began to disappear with the coming to our shores of the Industrial Revolution roughly a century ago; we are losing them at an accelerated rate since the full impact of the scientific revolution hit us about two decades ago. Directly or indirectly it has been the new technology these revolutions brought into being that altered the pattern of national life in ways that are detrimental to the democratic process. The many benefits we gain through technology come at a cost.

Let me briefly run over some of the advantages we have lost. Free land is gone, and we now have an excess, not a scarcity, of people as measured by available jobs. The self-employed have dwindled to 10% of the working population and grow fewer each year. The solid and real property, which once gave Americans what Socrates called a "private station" from which to exercise their rights as citizens, has been replaced by masses of possessions being paid for on the installment plan. It was Kenneth Galbraith, I believe, who noted that the average family is three weeks from bankruptcy, should the breadwinner lose his job.

Early visitors to America were amazed that we had neither paupers nor very rich men; we now have both. The richest 1% of our population owns 28% of the national wealth; the poorest 10% owns but one per cent. The gap is greater here than in many democracies abroad. We have some of the worst slums; one-fourth to one-fifth of our people live in want; and a substantial percentage are so poorly educated that we can find no jobs they are able to fill.

With the closing of the frontier a way of life came to an end that was simple and uncomplicated and therefore comprehensible to everyone. To make the wilderness habitable took a vast amount of rough work, so there was always demand for the kind of labor most people are able to perform. One needed little book learning to be successful in life. Men were scarce so they felt needed and therefore important. Public issues could be understood by ordinary men; de Tocqueville was astounded by the lively interest in politics he found here. "If an American were condemned to confine his activity to his own affairs, he would be robbed of one-half of his existence," he wrote in the 1830's.

What changed all this was technology. The technical level of a society always determines the range of occupational skills that are in demand. In preindustrial America, this range corresponded closely to the actual capabilities of our people. Today it is at odds with what one might call the natural range of competences. While men worked much harder in the past to earn a living, they needed much less formal schooling. Many people find it difficult or impossible to meet educational requirements that are indispensable at the present level of technology. The minimum now is a high school diploma. Though this is a modest level of education, nearly half our youth fail to achieve it. Yet it is not too much to ask; it is no more than is asked of workingmen in other advanced industrial countries.

To function properly in his environment a worker now needs to be a human being with a good basic education; he must certainly be wholly literate and what the English call numerate. Uneducated workers are a positive menace in complex industrial installations. Time and again I have seen production schedules delayed, countless hours of labor by highly skilled scientists and engineers brought to nothing, thousands of dollars' damage done by a single careless act of an uneducated worker.

Though we save ourselves much unpleasant

labor by means of technology, we have to exert ourselves more than in the past to reach the competencies required of all who are involved with technology. If, as I said before, decision-makers now should have a liberal education as well as professional competence, so must workers have a basic education in addition to their specific vocational skill. This is the price we have to pay for the many good things technology can provide.

But the raising of educational levels is not limited to job requirements. It is also essential to the discharge of our responsibilities as democratic citizens. Where in the past, life itself developed in most Americans the wisdom and experience they needed to reach intelligent opinions on public issues and to choose wisely among candidates for public office, we must today acquire this competence largely through studies that many people do not find particularly congenial. Yet unless one understands the world he lives in, including issues requiring political solutions, he is not a productive, contributing member of society. Uneducated citizens are potentially as dangerous to the proper functioning of our democratic institutions as are uneducated workers when they handle complicated machinery.

Paradoxically, liberal education, which at one time we tended to regard as "aristocratic," is the very kind of education we now need most to preserve our "democratic" way of life. Since it seeks to develop all the potentialities of the individual, not merely those he needs to earn a living, liberal or humanistic education shapes or forms him into a more capable, a more observant, a more discriminating human being. This he needs to be if he is to cope with the huge public and private power conglomerates that now dominate our society and interpose themselves between the American people and the men elected to public office, making it increasingly difficult for the popular will to assert itself whenever it goes counter to the interests of large organizations.

This is particularly serious when the people find they *must* call on their government to protect them against misuse of technology by one or another of these large organizations. So great is the power of these organizations that normally the interest of the sovereign people in getting protective laws enacted *and enforced* does not carry as much weight as the interest of organizations in continuing their harmful practices. Often something in the nature of a catastrophe which causes a public outcry will alone get action—the tragic case of the Thalidomide babies comes to mind. One could cite numerous examples of delayed or emasculated legislation and of inadequate enforcement of existing laws: for instance, against sale of foods and drugs containing ingredients not properly tested for side effects; against dangerous pesticides and weed killers which poison fish, plants and wildlife, and upset the ecological balance of nature; against air and water pollution.

The problem of how to limit power so men may be free is perennial and cumulative. No sooner is society organized to control one kind of power, than new ones appear, ranging themselves alongside the old power. The founders of our nation solved the problem as it then existed, that is, they limited the power wielded by government. Our problem is additionally to prevent the power of *bureaucratic organizations* from being used in ways that diminish individual liberty and undermine the democratic process. If we succeed in this we shall benefit from technology without having to sacrifice our precious heritage—freedom.

CYBERNETICS AND MARXISM-LENINISM

Maxim W. Mikulak

IN THE COURSE OF THE NINETEENTH CENTURY it became clear that philosophy and the empirically based sciences belong to distinct intellectual domains. However, in the Soviet Union it is asserted that natural science can only draw its correct "theoretical conclusions" by relying upon the philosophic and the methodological teachings of dialectical materialism. Certain Soviet Marxists have, on allegedly philosophic grounds, rejected Western genetics, the resonance theory of the chemical bond, the principle of uncertainty of quantum mechanics, relativist cosmology, the relativization of space, time, and matter, probability theory, and symbolic logic. The intriguing question remains whether Soviet dialectical materialists determine the validity of scientific theories and accomplishments on the basis of a priori judgments derived from philosophic analysis or whether the Soviet attacks on Western scientific thought are more political and ideological in nature.

The Soviet treatment of cybernetics, which was not immediately accepted by Soviet authorities in philosophy and science as a legitimate area of scientific inquiry, provides us with an insight into the working relationship between a given science and the *Weltanschauung* of dialectical materialism. In 1948 Norbert Wiener published his ground-breaking *Cybernetics, or Control and Communication in the Animal and the Machine,* and two years later *The Human Use of Human Beings,* stressing the social consequences of cybernetics, but it was only in 1958 that these two works were translated into Russian and made generally available to the Soviet scientific and philosophic communities. In 1953 the editors of the second edition of the *Bol'shaia sovetskaia entsiklopediia* failed to take cognizance of the existence of cybernetics. This omission was rectified on April 29, 1958, with the publication of a supplementary volume to the Soviet encyclopedia carrying A. N. Kolmogorov's factual presentation of the development of cybernetics. Whether by coincidence or design, it was also in 1958 that the first Soviet technical journal devoted exclusively to cybernetics, *Problemy kibernetiki,* made its debut. It required an additional two years, however, before the well-known and highly respected *Doklady* (Papers) of the USSR Academy of Sciences listed for the first time the topic "Cybernetics and the Theory of Regulation."[1] Why the Soviet delay in accepting cybernetics as a bona fide science?

The postwar Soviet hostility toward Western science in general is readily traceable to the ideological policy adopted by the Central Committee of the All-Union Communist Party. In 1945 the theoretical and political journal of the Party, *Bol'shevik,* noted that "socialist" and "bourgeois" science had little in common.[2] The following year a leading article in the same publication stated that all forms of Soviet social consciousness—science, art, philosophy, law, and so forth—be geared to the building of communism and acknowledge the correct version of Soviet reality.[3] A member of the Politburo, Andrei A. Zhdanov, was assigned the task of translating the Party line on ideological questions into a program of action. He was most instrumental in purging Soviet artistic and intellectual life of capitalistic survivals and of safeguarding Marxism-Leninism-Stalinism from subversion. In June, 1947 his crude assault on bourgeois science signaled a broad campaign for the ideological purification of Soviet science, the high point being the well-publicized suppression of Western genetics and Soviet geneticists. Thus the Soviet atmosphere that first greeted Wiener's cybernetics was most unreceptive to Western theoretical developments.

From 1950 to 1953 at least three pieces that encouraged Soviet antagonism respecting cybernetics theory were published. The first, "Against Idealism in Mathematical Logic," by V. P. Tugarinov and L. E. Maistrov, was in the judgment of some Soviet writers to be directly detrimental to the advancement of mathematical logic and indirectly harmful to the progress of information theory. Essentially these two authors attacked a Russian translation of a German text on the fundamentals of theoretical logic by D. Hilbert and V. Ackerman, chided the Soviet historian and philosopher of mathematics S. A. Ianovskaia for her academic sterility, and vilified the "idealist" views of B. Russell and A. N. Whitehead, which supposedly led mathematical logic to a cul-de-sac. The criticisms of Tugarinov and Maistrov have all the earmarks of being a formalistic ideological exercise instead of a serious analysis of mathematical logic proper.[4] In the second piece, which appeared in the widely circulated newspaper, *Literaturnaia gazeta,* M. Iareshevsky condemned cybernetics as a science of obscurantists and a pseudoscience wedded to idealist epistemology.[5] The most vituperative diatribe on cybernetics was produced by an anonymous "Materialist" who considered Wiener's brain-child a form of "atomic sociology" surrounded by "mysterious forces" of imperialist technology. He could not comprehend how one scientific discipline could cut across remote control, self-regulation, and servo-mechanization as well as biology, physiology, psychology, psychopathology, sociology, and political economics. This anonymous writer believed that the process of applying cybernetics to living organisms and to human society smacked of pure mysticism.[6]

At first appearance the Soviet philosophers and ideologues seem to have been responsible for creating Soviet resistance to Wiener's theory of communication and control. The Soviet scientists S. L. Sobolev, A. I. Kitov, and A. A. Liapunov definitely contributed to this impression when they disclosed that it was primarily Soviet philosophers who insisted on labeling cybernetics an idealistic pseudoscience. These three scientists were convinced that some thinkers rejected cybernetics because they were unaware of its scientific core and because the philosophers equated Wiener's theory with popularized Western versions of cybernation that indulged in sensationalism and speculation. This, in turn, led Marxist-Leninist writers to misinterpret cybernetics, to greet its progress with silence, and to neglect its remarkable achievements.[7] Years later the internationally renowned Russian physicist P. L. Kapitsa underscored the role of the philosophers in the theory of control and communication by pointing out the pejorative definition of cybernetics in the 1954 Soviet *Filosofskii slovar'*: "a form of reactionary pseudoscience originating in the United States after World War II and now widely employed in other capitalist countries; a form of contemporary mechanization." Academician Kapitsa emphasized that if the scientists had taken the Soviet philosophers' view on cybernetics at face value, the Soviet Union would never have been in a position to conquer space.[8]

G. V. Platonov acknowledged that Soviet scientists were just as guilty as the philosophers in approaching modern science, including cybernetics, with a "nihilistic" outlook.[9] D. N. Menitsky explicitly stated that Soviet biologists had opposed cybernetics because of the extravagant claims made for this new science in Western publications and because they were simply ignorant of the revolutionary contributions of mathematics, physics, and chemistry to biological cybernetics.[10] Ernest Kol'man, himself a philosopher of science, noted the nihilistic state of mind of some of his colleagues toward cybernetics and other branches of Western science. The opponents of cybernetics no longer referred to the theory of control and communication in the machine and living organism as pseudoscience but now argued that it was identical to automation and therefore deserved no separate title to existence. It was apparent to Kol'man from the sessions on automation sponsored by the Soviet Academy of Sciences in October, 1956 and from the discussions held by the Moscow Mathematical Society in April, 1957 that the very same engineers, technicians, and mathematicians who were furthering automation opposed Wiener's cybernetics and that the narrow specialists in biology, physiology, psychology, and linguistics could not reconcile themselves to cybernetics because it represented a "misalliance" of incongruous disciplines.[11]

In 1954 a new Party line was promulgated for

Soviet philosophy and science. The Party publication *Kommunist* emphasized that practice must serve as the highest and most reliable criterion for evaluating the truth of scientific propositions. At its plenary sessions of February and March, 1954 the Party Central Committee sharply criticized dogmatism in the agricultural sciences—an allusion to the 1948 genetics controversy. The Marxist-Leninist philosophers, so often coddled by the Party leadership, were castigated for being unproductive in the area of philosophy and science.[12] The able Soviet physicist S. L. Sobolev, backing the Central Committe's position, remarked that a clash of opinions and freedom of criticism were vital to the progress of the sciences. He saw in dogmatism the true enemy of science, especially in Soviet genetics.[13] It was obvious that the ideological policy associated with Andrei Zhdanov had run its course.

There was no intention of severing dialectical materialist philosophy from the Soviet natural sciences. That the Party opposed dogmatism in the sciences is unquestioned, but it also opposed any manifestations of philosophic neutralism. Party spokesmen made it abundantly clear that dialectical materialism was absolutely indispensable for Soviet scientists; it would save them from making idealistic interpretations of scientific data and of reality and keep them from undue deference to bourgeois science. But a nihilistic outlook that found nothing of value in capitalistic science was repudiated as anti-Leninist. The Party leadership made it plain that Soviet science was to grow and prosper on the granite foundation of Marxism-Leninism and that Soviet scientists were to struggle against indifference to its "principles on the scientific front."

What impact did the new Party line have on cybernetics? Although it is possible to find in Soviet literature mention of the rationalization of mental labor and of thinking machines as early as 1926,[14] the first significant Soviet defense of cybernetics was made by Kol'man in November 1954 at the Academy of Social Sciences attached to the Party's Central Committee. This Czech-born Soviet philosopher, who throughout his long career managed to avoid extremist stands on the philosophic issues of modern science, was competent to judge the worth of cybernetics.[15] In his lecture before the Academy, "What Is Cybernetics?" Kol'man belittled the detractors of cybernetics, noted the preparatory role played by Russian and Soviet scientists (Chernyshev, Shorin, Andronov, Kulebakin, Pavlov, Kolmogorov, Krylov, Bogoliubov, Markov, Novikov, and Shanin) in laying the foundation for cybernetics, and stressed the value of cybernetics for advancement of human thought.[16] Soon thereafter, Sobolev, Kitov, and Liapunov published their paper presenting in favorable light the basic concepts underlying cybernetics.[17]

Despite the Party's stand on dogmatism in science and despite the Central Committee declaration at its 1955 plenary session on the necessity of utilizing automation and cybernetic technology, the immediate response of Soviet intellectuals to Wiener's theory was less than enthusiastic. A few articles and pamphlets in popular vein were published. Some excellent work on information theory was carried out by A. Ia. Khinchin, A. N. Kolmogorov, and A. A. Liapunov. Some of the philosophical and physiological aspects of cybernetics were studied by P. K. Anokhin, B. Kh. Gurevich, and G. K. Khilme. Contributions on the practical application of self-regulating and control methods were most numerous. But for the most part all these contributions to the theory of information, control, and communication pursued lines of research characteristic of the pre-Wiener era: these studies did not advance the science of cybernetics but rather the separate disciplines of mathematics, physics, biology, physiology, and economics. Consequently, before 1958 cybernetics was not handled by most Soviet scientists as a distinct science having its own unique structure, methodology, and solutions. The practical problem of determining the relation of cybernetics to the other disciplines had to be solved first. Nevertheless, after 1954 no malicious attacks on cybernetics appeared in popular Soviet publications.

By 1958 cybernetics had been accepted as an area of scientific knowledge in the Soviet Union. Not only did the technical journal *Problemy kibernetiki* make its first appearance in 1958 under the editorship of Liapunov, but in April of that year the Scientific Council on Cybernetics was established by the Soviet Academy of Sciences and headed by Academician A. I. Berg. Thereafter, Soviet publications were inundated with pieces on the theory of communication, control, and information. The outstanding Western developers of cybernetics, W. R. Ashby, R. V. Z. Hartley, J. von Neumann, C. E. Shannon, N. Wiener, and many others, also had found acceptance by Soviet authorities. In the case of Wiener the popular Soviet magazine *Ogonek* virtually stated that it was criminal of Soviet philosophers to denounce the founder of cybernetics as an "obscurantist."[18] Subsequently, Wiener was sought out by Soviet scholars for his opinions on the relation of cybernetics to man and philosophy.[19] A 1961 collection of essays, *Cybernetics in the Service of Communism,* stands in marked contrast in tone and purpose to "Materialist's" article "Whom Cybernetics Serves," published eight years earlier in *Voprosy filosofii.* And in 1963 I. V. Novik was able to write that cybernetics was not an accidental occurrence but a "result of the progress of social practice and theory."[20]

Thus in an unusual display of decisiveness, the responsible leadership of the Party endorsed the development of cybernetics in connection with automation. The Party, of course, saw in automation and cybernation the means of attaining an economy of abundance. At the Twentieth Congress (1956) a directive was issued for a program to complete the automation of Soviet plants.[21] The same line was taken three years later by the Twenty-first Congress. And at the Twenty-second Congress, in 1961, the need was voiced for expanding cybernetics studies in order to create the material-technical base for Communism.[22] Khrushchev personally advanced this line at all of these congresses. As a matter of fact, the president of the Ukrainian Academy of Sciences, B. Paton, stated that the Academy's Cybernetics Institute was following Khrushchev's advice, given at the Kiev Communist Party and economic *aktiv* in December, 1962, stressing the "necessity for developing research in cybernetics and for using computers in accounting and planning in the national economy."[23] At the same time, however, the Party was demanding that Western science be examined in the light of dialectical materialism. What were the consequences?

Even though the scientific principles of cybernetics achieved an aura of respectability in the Soviet Union, its ideological and philosophic content, as expounded by Western writers, was not completely acceptable to Soviet dialectical materialists. The philosophers and scientists who backed cybernetics in Soviet Russia were among the first to condemn some of the philosophic views of Western cyberneticians. Wiener was variously accused of pragmatism,[24] antiscientism,[25] vulgar materialism,[26] natural-history materialism,[27] positivism, and idealistic eclecticism.[28] The neurophysiologist, Grey W. Walter, was labeled a mechanist.[29] W.

Ross Ashby's interpretation of cybernetics was stigmatized as mechanistic materialism bordering on idealism, irrationalism, and indeterminism.[30] To make matters more confusing, S. Anisimov and A. Vislobokov asserted that cybernetics became a disreputable subject in the hands of bourgeois spiritualists who used it to prove the existence of God and the immortality of the soul.[31] On the other hand, Kol'man mentioned on several occasions that Western ecclesiastics spurned cybernetic theory because they believed that inherent in its teachings was the idea that machines could be created having some of the attributes of living organisms.[32] Other criticisms were that the capitalistic view of cybernetics led to reactionary philosophic and sociological conclusions and that automation played an exploitative role in the class struggle existing in bourgeois society.[33] Despite the fact that Wiener, Ashby, and other Western cyberneticians lacked a consistent philosophic outlook, Soviet Marxists were not to discard cybernetics for its inadequate methodological and philosophic development. On the contrary, Soviet Marxist philosophers were urged to provide the proper dialectical materialist interpretation for cybernetics so that it could rest securely on a scientific base.[34]

One of the main problems facing Soviet philosophers was to define the function and scope of cybernetics. The possibility that cybernetics represented a serious challenge to the monopolistic position of a dialectical materialism in the Soviet

Union was studied. Soviet writers were aware that some Western authors had made fantastic claims, in effect describing cybernetics as a new philosophy of universal application in solving problems stemming from the world of nature and from human society. According to Soviet Marxists only dialectical materialism can provide the most general laws of development of the natural world and the human social order, and this assertion is in harmony with Engels' definition of dialectics as "the science of the most general laws of *all* motion." These general laws of motion are the triadic Hegelian laws of thought: the law of the transformation of quantity into quality and vice versa, the law of the unity and the struggle of opposites, and the law of the negation of the negation. The Hegelian laws are supposed to be abstracted from nature, human society, and thought and to reflect the most general interconnections found in nature, society, and thinking.[35] As a result, Soviet Marxists were forced to conclude that cybernetics at best was much more narrow in its spectrum of applicability than dialectical materialism. Furthermore, it was agreed that the theory of control and communication could not be construed as a form of materialist philosophy although it might have implications for philosophy.[36]

Having thus decided that cybernetics was not a philosophy, Soviet Marxists proceeded to explore the uniqueness of the new and burgeoning science in order to determine whether it merited a title to separate existence or not. Undoubtedly many Soviet scientists saw in cybernetics and the traditional theory of control and communication a duplication of effort, since the traditional theory was well established before Wiener's entrance into this area. Nonetheless, Z. Rovensky, A. I. Uemov, and E. K. Uemova admitted that, although cybernetics included the fields of physics, biology, mathematics, electronics, and sociology, its uniqueness lay in the fact that it was not a part of any of these branches of science.[37] B. S. Ukraintsev also recognized that cybernetics impinged on several areas of science, yet agreed in principle that cybernetics had its own subject matter.[38] Iu. I. Sokolovsky believed it wiser to discuss the sphere of influence of cybernetics rather than its contents.[39] In the opinion of Anisimov and Vislobokov cybernetics achieved the status of a special science when Wiener compared electronic networks with nervous systems; they stated that the real problem of cybernetics arose not in relation to automation but in relation to physiology, psychology, linguistics, and economics.[40] But the consensus among Soviet scholars now is that cybernetics is a separate science primarily concerned with the processes of controlling and directing the storage, transmission, and reworking of information in the machine and the biological organism.[41]

Soviet philosophers have not as yet established to their own satisfaction any clear relationship between cybernetics and the other sciences, nor have they sharply delineated the area of operation for cybernetics.[42] Part of the difficulty in ascertaining the scientific status of cyberntics is rooted in the Soviet Marxist adherence to the scheme of the classification of science devised by Engels. He divided knowledge into the three traditional areas of the exact physical sciences, the descriptive biological sciences, and the historical social sciences, in terms of the forms of motion exhibited by the objects under investigation.[43] He wrote: "*Classification of the sciences,* each of which analyzes a single form of motion, or series of forms of motion that belong together and pass into one another, is therefore the classification, the arrangement, of these forms of motion themselves according to their inherent sequence, and herein lies its importance."[44] Thus mechanics is derived from a study of celestial and terrestrial motion, physics and chemistry from molecular motion, and the plant and animal sciences from organic activity. Cybernetics, if defined as the general laws of control and direction in machine, organism, and society, simply does not fit neatly into Engels' scheme. The Rumanian scholar I. N. Belenescu pinpointed the following characteristics of matter in motion: (1) all motion exists in time and space; (2) all forms of motion involve the interactions of things and events; and (3) all forms of motion contain within themselves contradictions and a unity of contradictions, and a unity of continuity and non-continuity. In his estimation Wiener's cybernetics did not possess any particular form of motion of its own; therefore, it could not be treated as a science in the same sense as physics, chemistry, and biology.[45] Pursuing Belenescu's thinking to its logical conclusion, Ukraintsev, in 1961, did not anticipate that cybernetics would make any new discoveries or establish any new laws of moving matter.[46] Strictly speaking, in the Soviet Union cybernetics cannot be treated as a singular scientific discipline unless Engels' approach to the classification of the sciences is abandoned.

At the heart of the problem of classifying cybernetics is the concept of information. Wiener's statement that "information is information, not matter or energy," is categorically rejected by Soviet philosophers. For a science to be materialist in the eyes of the Marxist-Leninist dialecticians it must reveal some link with material substances or energy (and energy is presumed to be a special form of moving matter). The general Soviet position is that information is connected with material processes as thinking is connected with the brain. It is inconceivable to most Soviet Marxists that information can exist without the presence of physical activity.[47] F. P. Tarasenko went so far as to say that information is a property of matter and connected with matter.[48] In agreement with other Soviet authors he believed that the signal is the material carrier of information. And P. K. Anokhin equated the theory of information with the theory of signals.[49] I. V. Novik not only believed that information is a product of matter, but also he attempted to link the concept of information with Lenin's epistemological theory of reflections (sensations and concepts are "reflections" or "copies" of material objects).[50] As a consequence of the materialistic conception of information, Soviet cybernetics concentrates on the physical systems of control and direction.

To complicate the situation further, information is not only a product of physical activity, but it also has a mathematically structured form. The mathematical features of the theory of information are fully recognized by Soviet scientists and philosophers.[51] Both mathematics and the theory of information are used to establish quantitative relationships of physical processes, but neither discipline per se contributes any laws governing the various forms of moving matter. Where do mathematics and the theory of information fit into Engels' classification of the sciences? Unfortunately for the Soviet philosophers, Engels offered no ready-made answers on the nexus of mathematics to the edifice of science. However, he postulated the existence of a science dealing with the laws of human thought and limited this science to logic and dialectics.[52] It can be argued that mathematics is a form of logic. Nevertheless, Soviet Marxists seemingly eschew this issue of classifying mathematics as a science of thought. What is more, Soviet dialectical materialists refuse to concede that the theory of information is as extensive in application as dialectical thought. Despite the fact that cybernetics defies classification within the framework of Engels' dialectical materialism, its development in Soviet Russia is closely associated with the mathematicians and is considered an offspring of mathematics.

The one area of philosophic inquiry that has attracted special Soviet attention concerns the similarities and differences between man and his machines, between living tissue and electronic circuitry. The question as to whether or not an electronic calculating machine can be constructed to reproduce the processes of the human brain has generated considerable discussion among Soviet scientists and philosophers. The starting point of this discussion was the imputation to machines, on the part of some Western writers, of the human-like experiences of thinking, remembering, problem-solving, creating, talking, and so on. It was acknowledged that cybernetics had forced a re-examination of many concepts and definitions of human behavior. While Soviet intellectuals generally agree that some of the operational features of electronic calculating machines *simulate* human behavior, they overwhelmingly stress that human beings and machines are basically dissimilar for the following reasons: man possesses consciousness, a machine does not; thinking is solely the product of the biological world and not evident in the mechanical world; organic processes differ qualitatively from machine processes; and human thinking and activity operate under social, psychological, and physiological laws whereas the machine operates under physical laws. From the dialectical materialist position no "equals" sign can be placed between man and machine.[53]

The nearly unanimous negative stand of the Soviet cyberneticians and philosophers on the question whether machines think or not is best understood against the background of the great philosophic controversies of the 1920s between the mechanistic materialists and the Hegelian dialecticians. In 1926 at the Institute of Scientific Philosophy a discussion was held on Bergson's philosophy, vitalism, and reductionism. The Russian mechanistic materialists took the position that it was within the realm of possibility to reduce biological phenomena to the laws of chemistry and physics. The Hegelian Marxists denounced reductionism on the dialectical grounds that there are qualitative, and not merely quantitative, differences between living and nonliving matter. Engels himself wrote in *Dialectics of Nature* that the mechanical conception of nature "explains all change from change of place, all qualitative differences from quantitative ones and overlooks that the relation of quality and quantity is reciprocal, that quality can become transformed into quantity just as much as quantity into quality, that, in fact, reciprocal action takes place."[54] And he also stated that a living organism is *"the higher unity which within itself unites mechanics, physics, and chemistry into a whole* where the trinity no longer can be separated."[55] The Russian Hegelian dialecticians did not deny that biological processes contained simpler forms of motion, but they refused to assent to the notion that biological activity was the summation of chemical and physical forms of motion.[56] There is little to indicate that Soviet thinkers have deviated from the basic stand of Engels and the Russian dialecticians on reductionism. Soviet dialectical materialists of the current crop still support the conception of the unity of organic and inorganic processes whereby the more complex forms of motion have incorporated the simpler forms.[57] Although the question is seldom discussed, the Soviet Marxists apparently advocate a *hierarchic order of natural laws* in which the higher forms of moving matter are produced from lower forms with an accompanying qualitative change.

Few in the Soviet Union openly deny the validity of applying cybernetic concepts to both the physical and biological sciences. But this introduces the ticklish question of explaining how cybernetics bridges the gulf between the living and the nonliving without damaging the dialectical approach to reductionism. Thus L. A. Petrushenko was aware of the fact not only that cybernetic terminology is used in describing systems of control and direction in the living organism as well as the automated device but also that the principle of feedback and the theory of information are of vital importance in comprehending the operations of both the nervous system and the cybernetic machine. He was impressed with the universal nature of the process of feedback and designated it as the "motion of regulation" having the helically cyclical direction of dialectical motion itself.[58] Inasmuch as dialectical motion is evidenced throughout the natural world, it can be presumed that the "motion of regulation" is also ubiquitous.

D. N. Menitsky presented a more orthodox dialectical analysis of cybernetics as the bond between the biological and the exact sciences.[59] He asked whether there can be principles common to physics and biology. According to dialectical materialism each science exists because it isolates a facet of nature and studies a particular form of the movement of matter, but nature itself is not composed of isolated parts. It is in the interconnectedness of natural phenomena that general principles arise; else, how can the fields of biomechanics, biophysics, and biochemistry be justified? As for cybernetics, Menitsky stated that "its methods, built on mathematical logic, study only general principles without going into the qualitative characteristics of different phenomena." Consequently cybernetics was not directly identified with either the organic or the inorganic forms of matter. This thesis was shared by Academician A. I. Berg.[60] In classifying cybernetic notions under the heading of general principles, the problem of reconciling cybernetic concepts in terms of reductionism becomes irrelevant.

Another aspect of cybernetics, which at first glance does not seem to conform to the dialectical attitude toward reductionism, is the utilization of cybernetic physical models in explaining biological processes. The comparison of electronic systems with nervous systems is standard procedure in the Soviet Union.[61] Soviet cyberneticians and philosophers, however, severely circumscribe the applicability of physical concepts to biological phenomena. (Both Wiener and the French writer L. Couffignal have been criticized for equating the neuron with the relays of computers, and the nervous system with the diodes of electronic machines.)[62] Cybernetic models are regarded at most as analogous but never identical to biological operations. The Soviet scientist I. T. Frolov remarked that cybernetic models have heuristic value but are limited because they oversimplify complex biological systems.[63] Marxist philosopher B. S. Ukraintsev is convinced that analogies, no matter how useful, are methodologically unreliable in scientific research.[64] Kol'man considers cybernetic models tenable only if they are treated as approximating the nervous system; he believes that the use of physical models for the biological sciences is valid inasmuch as biology studies a form of matter in motion and all matter is subject to *physical* laws, but this in no sense implies that biology is reducible to physics.[65]

The fact that cybernetic principles and models are operative in organic and inorganic matter is attractive from the dialectical materialist point of view, for Soviet philosophers believe that the science of communications and control gave the *coup de grâce* to vitalism.[66] Unlike vitalism, it is argued, dialectical materialism and cybernetics reveal that the living and nonliving worlds are closely interrelated and that living matter contains within itself lower forms of motion. Furthermore, both dialectical materialism and cybernetics affirm the materiality of life processes and do not postulate any mystical *élan vital* separating the organic from the inorganic. In a sense, then, Soviet cybernetics is not seen as a triumph for vitalism or a victory for reductionism but a confirmation of the dialectical teaching of the interconnectedness and interpenetration of nature.

Too often Western observers of the Soviet scene have been inclined to regard ideological pronunciamentos hostile to a given scientific theory as amounting to a death warrant for that theory in the Soviet Union. Such a view generally overrates the role of the Marxist ideologist as an arbiter of Soviet science. Too often, also, Soviet ideologues have rejected a Western scientific theory not because of its scientific content but because of the philosophic conclusions associated with it. This view overrates the significance of the speculative, sensationalist, and often quite shallow statements appearing in the popular Western press. What *has* proved to be a source of continuing embarrassment to Soviet philosophers is that the scientific theories they have condemned as irreconcilable with dialectical materialism are subsequently accepted as confirming and enriching dialectical materialist doctrines. Such Western scientists as Einstein, Heisenberg, Pauling, Wiener, and others at first censured as idealists, obscurantists, and mystics by Soviet nihilistic Marxists are later credited by Soviet authorities with having made substantial contributions to science. These inconsistent Soviet practices respecting Western science have tended to debase dialectical materialism in Western eyes as a philosophy of science.

A major factor contributing to the ambivalent attitude of the Soviet Marxists toward science is their use of nonscientific criteria in evaluating the correctness or incorrectness of any scientific theory. Surprising as it may seem to Western scientists, Soviet philosophers and ideologues have been known to attack Western scientific theories because of a scientist's personal philosophy, his political outlook, his class background, or his lack of adherence to the dialectical propositions on nature and reality. To this day there is no definite and uniformly accepted Soviet formula on the relationship of dialectical materialism to the exact sciences, other than general statements that have little, if any, value in solving the real and practical problems of science. There is no Soviet philosophic substitute for mathematical and laboratory procedures as a means of ascertaining the validity of a scientific hypothesis. As long as Soviet Marxists employ a multiplicity of nonscientific standards in judging the truth of a scientific theory, and as long as the relationship between Marxist philosophy and the natural sciences is not elucidated concretely, there is bound to be uncertainty surrounding the application of dialectical materialism to the sciences.[67]

While cybernetics was ridiculed by some Soviet writers, work on symbolic, mathematical, and constructive (intuitional) logic continued virtually unimpeded during the 1930s and 1940s, especially by Markov, Shanin, Novikov, and Kolmogorov. As early as 1934 the Soviet Academy of Sciences had organized a commission on remote control and automatization. The year 1936 saw the introduction of the journal *Avtomatika i telemekhanika.*[68] In 1950 the Institute for Precision Mechanics and Computer Technology came into existence; its chief function was to develop the practical aspects of programming. And it took three volumes to record the reports made in 1953, at the Second All-Union Conference on the Theory of Automatic Regulation, on the progress of control technology from 1940 to 1953. Excellent textbooks on servomechanisms and control systems were written by B. S. Sotskov (1950), G. A. Shaumian (1952), and E. P. Popov (1956).[69] All these developments prove that Soviet scientists were furthering the growth of automation and cybernation at a time when symbolic logic and cybernetics were ostensibly under an ideological cloud.

After 1954 it was effectively argued by knowledgeable Soviet philosophers and scientists that cybernetics had never really been rejected on dialectical materialist grounds. As Soviet writers have themselves revealed, those who denied that cybernetics was a science did so out of ignorance and not out of philosophic considerations. The ideological campaign waged by Zhdanov was primarily an attempt to assert the superiority of the Soviet socialist system over the bourgeois West; it hardly merits attention as a *philosophic* campaign of profound significance for the Soviet sciences. Unless one equates Soviet ideology with dialectical materialism, there is little to support the contention that the scientific theory of control and communication was rejected on strictly philosophic grounds.

What has been the result of the interaction of dialectical materialist philsophy with Soviet cybernetics? Most important philosophically is that Soviet Marxists and scientists have managed to demonstrate the flexibility of dialectical materialism and its compatibility with cybernetics. Although Academician Berg assures us that "Soviet cybernetics is an independent science which leans upon the philosophy of dialectical materialism,"[70] Soviet dialecticians by and large have displayed no overt or direct influence on the evolution of the theory of control, communication, and information or on the mathematical and scientific problems connected with contemporary cybernation in the Soviet Union. The bulk of Soviet philosophic analysis has been focused on the definitional and philosophic aspects of cybernetics. Soviet dialectical materialism is adequate for resolving certain epistemological and philosophical questions arising from the interpretations of scientific knowledge, but it is ill-suited for establishing the truth of modern scientific theories. However, in the dialectical materialist storehouse there is the tenet that practice is the ultimate criterion of truth, and this tenet ultimately saves dialectical materialism from degenerating into a sterile body of first principles for weighing scientific truth.[71] Because cybernetics has proven its efficacy in actual practice, this science can be assured the continuing support of the Soviet Communist Party. And because of the criterion of practice Soviet Marxists had no choice but to reconcile cybernetics with dialectical materialist doctrines.

NOTES

1. Two comprehensive bibliographies of Soviet publications on cybernetics are available: D. D. Comey, "Soviet Publications on Cybernetics," *Studies in Soviet Thought,* 2 (1964), 142–61; L. R. Kerschner, "Western Translations of Soviet Publications on Cybernetics," *ibid.,* 162–77.
2. *Bol'shevik,* 11–12 (1945), 2.
3. *Ibid.,* 9 (1946), 5.
4. *Voprosy filosofii* (hereafter *VF*), 3 (1950), 331 ff.
5. April 5, 1952.
6. *VF,* 5 (1953), 210 ff.
7. *VF,* 4 (1955), 147 ff.

8. *Ekonomicheskaia gazeta,* March 26, 1962.

9. In *Dialekticheskii materializm i sovremennoe estestvoznanie* (Moscow: 1957), p. 22.

10. *Biophysics* (USSR), 2 (1957), 134 ff.

11. E. Kol'man, *Kibernetika* (Moscow: 1956), pp. 29–30; Kol'man in *Filosofskie voprosy kibernetiki* (hereafter *FVK*) (Moscow: 1961), p. 90.

12. *Kommunist,* 5 (1954), 3 ff.

13. *Pravda,* July 2, 1954.

14. *Pod znamenem marksizma,* 12 (1926), 72 ff.

15. In his *Kriticky ńyklad symbolicke metody moderni logiky* (Prague: 1948) Kol'man displayed a critical acquaintance with Western literature on symbolic logic.

16. *VF,* 4 (1955), 148 ff.

17. See note 7, above.

18. *Ogonek,* 16 (1959), 23.

19. *Priroda,* 8 (1960), 68; *VF,* 9 (1960), 164 ff.

20. I. Novik, *Kibernetika. Filosofskie i sotsiologicheskie problemy* (Moscow: 1963), p. 34.

21. *VF,* 6 (1959), 148.

22. *VF,* 11 (1962), 153.

23. *Izvestiia,* April 2, 1963.

24. *VF,* 4 (1955), 149.

25. VF, 3 (1957), 157.

26. *Filosofskie voprosy fiziki i khimii,* 1 (1959), 67.

27. *Vestnik Leningradskogo Universiteta, Seriia ekonomiki, filosofii i prava,* 17 (1960), 76.

28. In *FVK,* pp. 97–98.

29. *VF,* 3 (1957), 156.

30. *Ibid.,* 157.

31. *Kommunist,* 2 (1960), 109.

32. Kol'man, *Kibernetika,* p. 3; Kol'man in *FVK,* p. 86.

33. *VF,* 4 (1955), 147; *Avtomatika i telemekhanika,* 7 (1959), 999; *FVK,* p. 86.

34. *FVK,* p. 227.

35. F. Engels, *Dialectics of Nature* (Moscow: 1954), p. 353; Engels, *Anti-Dühring* (Moscow: 1954), pp. 195, 510; V. M. Kovalgin, *Dialekticheskii materializm o zakonakh nauki* (Minsk: 1958), pp. 88 ff; M. N. Rutkevich, *Dialekticheskii materializm* (Moscow: 1959), p. 280.

36. *VF,* 5 (1960), 54; *FVK,* pp. 25, 169, 231.

37. Z. Rovenskii *et al., "Mashina i mysl'" Filosofskie ocherk o kibernetike* (Moscow: 1960), p. 56.

38. In *FVK,* p. 111.

39. Iu. I. Sokolovskii, *Kibernetika nastoiashchego i budushchego* (Kharkov: 1959), p. 21.

40. *Kommunist,* 2 (1960), 108.

41. *Filosofskie problemy sovremennogo estestvoznaniia* (Moscow: 1959), pp. 237 ff; Kol'man, *Kibernetika,* p. 13; *FVK,* pp. 26, 97, 112 ff., 180, 182, 228.

42. Kol'man, *Kibernetika,* p. 13; *VF,* 4 (1957), 158.

43. Engels, *Anti-Dühring,* pp. 123–27; *Dialectics of Nature,* pp. 326–39.

44. Engels, *Dialectics of Nature,* p. 330.

45. *VF,* 3 (1957), 161.

46. In *FVK,* p. 111.

47. *Kommunist,* 2 (1960), 116; *FVK,* p. 115.

48. *VF,* 4 (1963), 78.

49. *VF,* 4 (1957), 153.

50. Novik, *Kibernetika,* pp. 58 ff.

51. Kol'man, *Kibernetika,* p. 13; *Kommunist,* 2 (1960), 110; *Nauchnye doklady vysshei shkoly, Filosofskie nauki,* 3 (1959), 100; *Vestnik Akademii nauk SSSR,* 9 (1957), p. 39; *Filosofskie problemy sovremennogo estestvoznaniia,* p. 237; *FVK,* p. 8.

52. Engels, *Anti-Dühring,* p. 127.

53. *VF,* 3 (1956), p. 119; *Filosofskie problemy sovremennogo estestvoznaniia,* p. 259; *Kommunist,* 2 (1960), 111; *Nauka i zhizn',* 2 (1960), 41; *VF,* 2 (1961), 103; 1, (1963), 36. It is interesting to note that the philosophically-minded Russian chemist I. Orlov raised similar objections in 1926 to a "thinking" machine demonstrated by Professor Shchukarov; see *Pod znamenem marksizma,* 12 (1926), 72 ff.

54. Engels, *Dialectics of Nature,* p. 335.

55. *Ibid.,* pp. 331–32.

56. *Pravda,* Aug. 1, 1926; *Pod znamenem marksizma,* 9–10 (1926), 89 ff.; A. Stliarov, *Dialekticheskii materializm i mekhanisty (nashi filosofskie raznoglasiia)* (Leningrad: 1930).

57. *Kommunist,* 2 (1959), 105; *Filosofskie voprosy fiziki i khimii,* 1 (1959), 63; *Nauka i zhizn',* 2 (1960), 41.

58. *Vestnik Leningradskogo Universiteta, Seriia ekonomiki, filosofii i prava,* 17 (1960), 76.

59. *Biophysics* (USSR), 2 (1957), 143.

60. In *FVK,* pp. 159 ff.

61. *VF,* 4 (1957), 142; 8 (1958), 92; 2 (1961), 39; 10 (1961), 92; 8 (1962), 78; *FVK,* pp. 123, 262–305, 338–45; *Pravda,* April 6, 1962.

62. *VF,* 3 (1957), p. 154.

63. *VF,* 2 (1961), 39–51.

64. In *FVK,* p. 123.

65. Kol'man, *Kibernetika,* pp. 31 ff.

66. *Nauka i zhizn',* 2 (1960), 41; *Vestnik Leningradskogo Universiteta, Seriia ekonomiki, filosofii i prava,* 17 (1960), 86; *VF,* 2 (1963), 70.

67. See my "Lenin on the 'Party' Nature of Science and Philosophy," in *Essays in Russian and Soviet His-*

tory (New York: 1963), pp. 164–76; "[Soviet] Philosophy and Science," *Survey,* 52 (1964), 147–56.

68. *Vestnik Akademii nauk SSSR,* 2 (1936), 64; A. A. Voronov, *Elementy teorii avtomaticheskogo regulirovaniia* (Moscow: 1954), pp. 6 ff.

69. *Trudy vtorogo vsesoiuznogo soveshchaniia po teorii avtomaticheskogo regulirovaniia* (Moscow and Leningrad: 1955); B. S. Sotkov, *Elementy avtomaticheskoi i telemekhanicheskoi apparatury* (Moscow and Leningrad: 1950); G. A. Shaumian, *Avtomaty* (Moscow: 1952); E. P. Popov, *Dinamika sistem avtomaticheskogo regulirovaniia* (Moscow: 1956).

70. In *FVK,* pp. 178–179.

71. Every important Soviet textbook on Marxism-Leninism has a section devoted to practice as the criterion of truth; see V. I. Lenin, *Materialism and Empirio-Criticism* (Moscow: 1952), pp. 136 ff.; F. V. Konstantinov, *et al., Osnovy marksistskoi filosofii* (Moscow: 1960), pp. 320 ff.; *Fundamentals of Marxism-Leninism* (Moscow: 1963), pp. 109 ff.

SOVIET CYBERNETICS AND INTERNATIONAL DEVELOPMENT

John J. Ford

A SWEEPING TECHNOLOGICAL AND INTELLECTUAL revolution is transforming contemporary society. It is not confined by national or geographic boundaries. The abilities, thoughts, and beliefs of men everywhere are being reshaped by forces which are the result of applied rationality. Norbert Wiener connoted the pattern of these changes with the word "cybernetics," a neologism which has become a general reference term for the contemporary revolution in industrial societies and a portent of the future for developing nations.

But the producers of these changes are neither witting revolutionaries nor avowed cyberneticists; they are scientists and engineers doing their jobs. To most of them cybernetics signifies, perhaps, a cult but not a scientific or engineering discipline nor even a branch of philosophy. Some popular writers view the result of such work as a new "spectre that is haunting the world."

To a growing minority throughout the world, however, cybernetics has come to serve as a conceptual vantage point for the comprehension of the whole of technological progress and for the rational development of the accompanying social reality.

If cybernetics is of significance to international society it will be in terms of an experimental approach to a lessening of the chaos accompanying social transitions in the developing nations. As yet, however, sociopolitical processes have not been viewed very extensively from the standpoint of cybernetics. The massive experiment of Soviet scientists to test the applicability of cybernetics to the engineering of total social system transition has been underway for an insufficient time to warrant even preliminary conclusions.

THE SOVIET EXPERIMENT

The Soviet experiment, however, illustrates the magnitude of effort necessary for such a program and the commensurate reward foreseen if its pursuit proves successful. Cybernetics began to be discussed in the Soviet Union about 1953. By 1959 the Soviets had begun to organize a cybernetics program. This nationwide effort is addressed to the automation of many dimensions of social reality:

industry, transportation, medical diagnosis, power systems, economics, law, and education. The program is based on the Soviet belief that automation of social functions is required to achieve the increased organizational complexity necessary for social progress or development. Soviet cybernetics encompasses the totality of efforts devoted to the engineering of social progress or development.

The beginnings of the Soviet program in cybernetics lay in an ideological controversy that almost induced a national psychosis in the USSR.[1] After 1955 the arguments polarized into two major positions. At one extreme were some of the natural scientists and Party dogmatists championed by certain literary figures who were trying to perpetuate the traditional separation of the sciences along with the Marxian view of social development. At the other pole was a group of mathematicians and technologists fostering cybernetics as a unifying science and as a tool for directing social process.

The 22nd Congress of the CPSU in 1961 seemed to resolve the polemic in favor of the pro-cybernetics camp. The Twenty-Year Plan for the Transition to Communism ratified by the Congress declared that:

> The introduction of highly perfected systems of automatic control will be accelerated. It is *imperative* to organize wider application of cybernetics, electronic decision-making computer devices and control installations in pro-

> duction, research work, drafting and designing, planning, accounting, statistics and state management.[2]

Of far greater significance than the polemic in the Party press was the intellectual turmoil stirred up by cybernetics in the scientific community. Representatives of the special sciences refused at first to accept the notion that the problems of control and communication provided a common thread by which the separate sciences could be tied together. But eventually even the most articulate among the defenders of academic pigeon-holes came to express—if not to believe—that physical scientists, engineers, life scientists, mathematicians, and social scientists shared a cybernetics-based commonality.[3]

The first locus of the intellectual upheaval fomented by cybernetics was the Academy of Social Sciences, an appendage of the Central Committee of the CPSU.[4] This Academy sponsored a continuous seminar on cybernetics during 1958–59 in collaboration with the Institute of Automatics and Telemechanics. Among the results of this seminar published in 1961[5] are papers which attempt to develop an understanding of the multidisciplinary content, scope of applicability, and the other equally broad problems of cybernetics, such as its implications for labor, physiology, and automatic control engineering.

Other seminars were created to deal with cybernetic problems arising out of specific scientific areas. Such forums were sponsored at the following components of the Academy of Sciences, USSR: the Physical Institute, the Mathematics Institute, the Institute of Biological Physics, the Institute of Radio Technology and Electronics, the Institute of Automatics and Telemechanics, the Institute of Chemical Physics, the Institute of Applied Geophysics, the Institute of Geology for the Development of Fuel Minerals, and the Institute of Atmospheric Physics.[6]

These institute seminars were consolidated during 1962 at the Joint Conference on Methodological Problems of Cybernetics.[7] More than 1000 specialists representing 30 of the largest industrial and scientific centers of the USSR participated: philosophers and mathematicians, physicists and biologists, engineers and linguists, psychologists and physicians. A complete record of this conference is unavailable but the conference's conclusions are presented by Mayzel' and Fatkin[8] and a collection of papers was published in 1964 in response to a decision of the joint conference. Entitled *Kibernetika, Myshleniye, Zhizn (Cybernetics, Thought, and Life),* this collection was prepared by the Cybernetics Section of the Scientific Council on Cybernetics of the Presidium, Academy of Sciences, USSR in collaboration with the Institute of Philosophy of the Academy.

The joint conference and its ensuing publications seem to have quelled much of the turmoil in the scientific community. The weight of numerous intellectual giants of the USSR was thrown to the side of cybernetics; among those in affirmation were A. A. Markov, A. A. Lyapunoy, S. V. Yablonskiy, Ye. N. Sokolov, V. M. Glushkov, and A. A. Feldbaum. Then, too, recognition in a document published with the approbation of the Party that cybernetics was of "fundamental Weltanschauung significance" calmed the less adventuresome scientists who had foreseen essential antagonisms between cybernetics and previous Party dogma.

But *Kibernetika, Myshleniye, Zhizn* does not kick over a lot of ideological traces; it merely explores and defines the subject matter of cybernetics and insists that Soviet successes in cybernetics are prerequisite to realization of the goals of Soviet society. The subject matter of cybernetics is said to include three main areas of control: control of systems of machines, technological processes, and processes in general which occur in the directed actions of man on nature; control of the activity of social groups organized to solve assigned problems (economic, financial, legal, transportation, military, and other groups' or organizations' operations); and control of the processes which occur in living organisms (physiological, biochemical, and other processes connected with vital activity).

Academician Admiral A. I. Berg, the editor of the volume, ties cybernetics to the goal-seeking activity of the state. He emphasizes in his introduction the breadth of cybernetics when considered as a science dealing with general laws regulating control processes in nature, in human society, and in production. But Berg justifies its development. The building of a communist society, he says, does not happen spontaneously but results from the purposeful application of science to its accomplishment. Berg claims that cybernetics is the key science for dealing with the overall purposeful guidance of the total process of social development.[9]

CYBERNETICS AND THE SOCIAL SCIENCES

Berg's linking of cybernetics as a science and technology to the concept of controlled social progress brings together the output of the natural science circles with the results of parallel activities involving the social scientists of the USSR and of the other Bloc nations. At present only a silhouette of the theory being evolved as the result of this activity is discernible, projected on a background of clichés. But because of its potential significance to the future of international society this theory of development, as it is called, needs to be adumbrated.

Social phenomena in a cybernetics context were discussed for the first time during 1958 in *Problemy Filosofii* by Arab-Ogly.[10] He presented a somewhat naive argument in support of the thesis that cybernetics can be a boon to applied sociology in socialistically organized societies but a bane to sociologists in the capitalist's world. The manner of presentation suggests that this position was advanced merely as a necessary accompaniment to the real message the author wished to convey, i.e., that

Soviet planners had a crying need for the development of a quantitative sociology and that computers and the methodologies thereof were indispensable in meeting that requirement.

A brochure giving clear outlines of an evolving theory of development was published in Poland by Oskar Lange in 1960 under the title *Totality, Development, and Dialectics in the Light of Cybernetics.* Three years later, the State Publishing House for Political Literature, Moscow, released the first Soviet brochure on the subject, *Cybernetics: Philosophical and Sociological Problems,* by I. Novik. Also during 1963 a number of articles by Soviet authors outlined their views on the relationship of cybernetics to social progress. This collection[11] authored by Academicians S. G. Strumilin, V. A. Trapeznikov, and V. S. Nemchinov reiterates much of what had been said already in many places: (1) an essentially new type of social organization will result from the application of science to society, and cybernetics is the best illustration of this relationship between science and the activity of people, a relationship to which the future belongs; (2) the industry of the future will undoubtedly be a complex of production processes united by a single automatic control and guidance system, with cybernated devices doing most of the work for man; and (3) when society passes from the basically primitive forms of control to automated systems based on scientific methods of research and electronic techniques, definite changes will result in the socioeconomic structure of society. These phrases have a familiar ring, but they are significant in that this "line" is put forth in an international journal by a group made up of a classical communist theoretician (Strumilin), the director of the Institute of Automatics and Telemechanics and official in the International Federation of Automatic Control (Trepesnikov), and the (then) head of the Economic Section of the Cybernetics Council. In retrospect, it seems that this collection was in a way an approbation to creative, non-Soviet thinkers and a forewarning of ideological developments brewing in the USSR.

Also during 1963 two relatively unknown Leningrade authors published a brochure, *Miracle of Our Time—Cybernetics and Problems of Development,* which closely parallels the work of Lange published three years earlier. The authors, B. V. Akhlibininskiy and N. I. Khralenko, analyze the reasons for the appearance of cybernetics as an independent branch of science, the role of cybernetics in the creation of the material-technical base of communism, and the contributions of cybernetics to understanding the essence of life and social dynamics. These threads are woven together in a popular style into what they call a "theory of development or progress."

In the spring of 1964 a conference on Cybernetics, Planning, and Social Progress was convened at the Novosti Preses Agency in Moscow. Sponsors of the meeting were the editors of *USSR,* the *Eko-*

nomicheskaya Gazeta and *Voprosy Ekonomiki*. The participants included leading Soviet mathematicians, philosophers, economists, chairmen of state committees, departments, and planning and statistical bodies, directors of research institutes, and heads of educational institutions. The theme of the meeting was the supposition that a socialist society can make use of cybernetics in ways "inconceivable" under other types of systems. Thus, if optimum efficiency in management is desired on the national scale, it is necessary to advance the development not only of cybernetics, but also of a social philosophy to guide its application. Foremost among the participants were V. M. Glushkov, Trapeznikov, Nemchinov, and other scientists intimately associated with the Cybernetics Council.[12]

Concurrent with the publication and meeting activity a joint seminar was initiated to develop a cybernetic methodology for the social sciences based on computer-based models of socioeconomic processes at the Department of Dialectical and Historical Materialism of Moscow University, in conjunction with the Cybernetics Council.

The latest contribution to the evolving cybernetics-related theory of development is a Czechoslovakian work, *Kybernetika ve Spolecenskych Vedach (Cybernetics in Sociological Research)*. Among the authors are Arab-Ogly, who wrote the first Soviet article dealing with cybernetics and society, and E. Kol'man, author of "What is Cybernetics?" the first favorable commentary on cybernetics published in the Soviet press.[13] These authors were pioneers in a movement to relate cybernetics and social dynamics, and, obviously, they have continued to work along these lines for the last decade.

THE THEORY OF DEVELOPMENT

The literature outlined in these chronologies dealing with cybernetics and the natural and social sciences reveals the skeleton of a theory of development. The following are some of the lemmas of this theory:

1. The most complex question connected with cybernetics is the problem of the direction of social change, and this question is equivalent to the question about the way in which the entropy of objects or phenomena in the surrounding world change. The world is not striving toward chaos and disorder; the predominant tendencies are toward systematization, toward increased levels of organization. Cybernetics is capable of giving the facts that foster this tendency. Together with philosophy, cybernetics is, therefore, the basis of the evolving theory of development.

2. Relative to the tendency of the change in entropy, it is possible to indicate two tendencies in structures, objects, and phenomena: on the one hand, they are striving to increased complexity of organization, and on the other, to simplification of that organization. The tendency of complication is equivalent to the accumulation of information; simplification, the reduction of information and,

correspondingly, the accumulation of entropy. The leading tendency is toward complication of organizational forms. In the language of information theory, then, the predominant tendency in the world is toward the accumulation of information, or increased negentropy, and correspondingly, reduced levels of entropy. In the development of society, each new stage in social development is a more complex form of organization than the preceding one. This accounts for increased orderliness and decreased chaos and disorder in social life.

3. If development or progress involves reduction of entropy and increases of negentropy, the isolation of a comparatively small number of objects in the system from other objects of the same type results in processes in that system which will lead to the simplification of the form of organization, to increased entropy. Retrogression of biological and social systems occurs when some parts thereof are isolated from other parts of such systems.

4. Development in biological evolution reveals the tendency toward complication in the organization of living systems and thereby facilitation of adaptation to environmental changes. Species which cannot achieve a stable, dynamically equilibrated, interrelation with their environments retrogress. Those systems progress which can maintain a homeostatic stability in relation to their environment. At certain levels of complexity of organization automatic feedback systems must evolve if homeostasis is to be maintained. In biological

evolution an example is provided by the system for maintaining the constancy of blood temperature, which accounted for the victory of warm-blooded animals in the struggle for survival.

5. Societies also develop by adaptation to changes in the environment, and, like biological systems, social systems produce changes in the conditions of their environment which are propitious for continued existence. As Vernadsky puts it, the "biosphere" adapts to conditions of the inorganic world and also substantially transforms it. In the development of biological species and to a much greater degree in the development of societies there is a tendency to replace the simple processes of adaptation to external conditions by the creation of new forms of external conditions which are more propitious in terms of survival.

6. The major tendency of social activity is toward the transformation of the environment in ways which correspond to human needs. The foremost component of this tendency is the social and production practices of the human members of the society, and in particular the production of tools with which to transform natural conditions to conform with the needs of society. Man deals not directly with nature, but with the nature that is being transformed by man. But in order for this to be possible, he must adapt to it. He does this not materially, like lower organisms that effect a change in themselves to adapt to the natural conditions, but ideally by making the content of his *ideas* con-

form to the arrangement of nature and its laws.

7. Cybernetics explains in the language of game theory why in the process of development complex organizational forms are better able to maintain stable conditions with the environment and hence to progress. A system reacts to an external influence with one of the methods at its disposal. Some systems have a single strategy for maintaining stability so that they respond to all external influences with a force directly proportional to the strength of the external stimulus. In such systems the greater the energy of internal links, the more stable the system will be. This is especially true of inorganic nature and of some types of animal behavior, i.e., the rabbit fleeing from danger or the withdrawal of the turtle's head in dangerous or unfamiliar situations.

A second method of achieving stability consists in meeting each strategy of the environment (opponent) with a new corresponding counterstrategy. The differences between responses are qualitative rather than quantitative, and the struggle for stability will be successful in direct proportion to the number of different strategies that the system has at its disposal—thus leading to the preservation of those systems which possess the greater variety of methods of behaving in response to varied external influences.

8. The variety of methods of behaving is equal to the store of information or negentropy. Thus the process of development is linked to organization,

information, and negentropy. The only system possessing a variety of strategies or a greater choice of possible responses is that one which has a complex inner structure, that is, a high level of organization. The more complex the system, the greater the choice of possible responses to external influences at its disposal. This is the reason why the basic path of biological and social progress is the complication of biological and social systems.

9. There are no upper limits to the level of complexity a system of organization may attain because the history of the development of living systems and society shows that the process of complication is accompanied by the development of mechanisms that simplify or "automate" complex systems. *Automation is, therefore, a universal law of development.* More than the automation of production processes is involved. The processes of control in living organisms, social systems, or the psyche lead in their development to automation. Automation creates that simplification without which further development would be impossible. Automation is simplification, but it is that kind of simplification which, in and of itself, represents a complex phenomenon.

10. Automation, insofar as it simplifies the interaction between complex systems, serves as a necessary condition for further complication, further development. But the problem of automating control in its most general sense is one of the central problems of cybernetics. Research, engineering, and applications of cybernetics to society are,

therefore, the key to the progressive development of society.

If the foregoing paragraphs correctly outline the evolving theory of development, Soviet mathematicians, engineers, mathematical economists, and so on, may increasingly work with a new breed of Communist social philosophers. One perceives, in recent Soviet articles that cybernetics has become a vantage point for scientists to generalize their activities and for social philosophers to concretize their ideas. This expectation is stated by I. V. Novik:

> The development of cybernetics again and again refutes the positivistic positions on the non-essentialness for natural science of general-philosophical positions on the world as a whole, and at the same time shows the *complete groundlessness and fallacy of the dogmatic approach* to the progress of the philosophical interpretations of the data of science.[14]

But cybernetics has become more than just a general concept for providing a mutual bridge between the scientists and philosophers. The decade of seminars on cybernetics led not only to a theory of development, but also to a research and development program to effect the optimal control of the social transition process.

THE CYBERNETICS RESEARCH AND DEVELOPMENT PROGRAM

Figure 1 depicts in a very abbreviated form the essential elements in purposeful systems which are objects of research for the Soviet cybernetics program. The real world is made up of cells, people, nations, factories, transportation systems, mines, and so on. Obviously, sensors are needed which are appropriate to detect changes in each system in the real world; eyes, radar, nerve endings, and pattern-recognition devices are examples. The information processors also differ depending on the type of information processed. Data sensed by the eyes is processed in the brain; information from radar sensors is processed by computers; and information from other types of sensors is transmitted to appropriate types of processors. Comparators receive processed information about some aspect of the behaving world and compare it with the kind of behavior called for by the reference model.

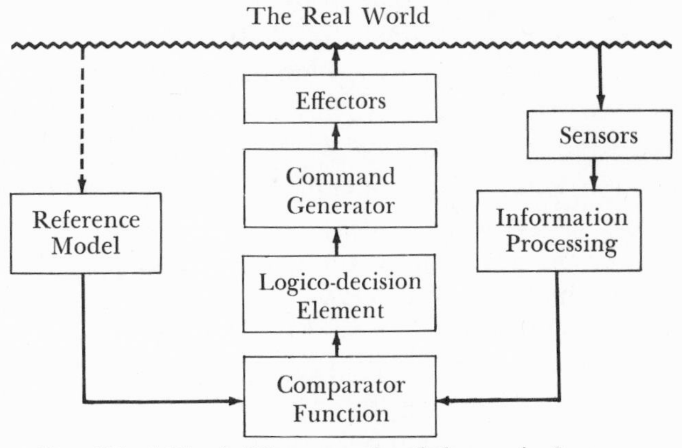

Simplified Block Diagram of a Cybernetic System.
Fig. 1.

The results of the comparison are transmitted to the command element, which then decides whether to leave the "real world" as it is or whether commands should be transmitted to the effectors to change the behavior of the real world. If the latter course is elected, information about the ensuing change is sensed, processed, compared with the reference model and so on around the feedback loop. Obviously an indefinitely large number of interconnected loops would be necessary to describe fully the organization of a system for the purposeful control of a total social system in the real world. But Fig. 1 does convey the essential notion that information about the real world is a necessary input to the effectors if the resulting control of the rate and direction of change is to be optimal in relation to the purpose dictated by the reference model of what "ought" to be.

Because information and control functions are the key features here, a common set of mathematical tools can be used in conjunction with the techniques of traditional sciences to study and to model them as they operate in living, technical, and social systems.

The Soviets manage their cybernetics program by having an administrative component assigning, monitoring, and directing research and development addressed to each subsystem in the real social world.

An *Izvestia* article of September 6, 1964 suggests the creation of a centrally managed national organization to foster efficiency of research and provide a central coordination mechanism to keep the directed change of each part of the social system in harmony with the transitions engineered in all other parts of the system. This "cybernetics industry" would be modelled after the Manhattan Project-like system devised for the Soviet nuclear energy program.

Fundamental research and engineering in cybernetics is managed by the Scientific Council for Cybernetics under the Presidium, Academy of Sciences, USSR. The Council has been directed by Academician Admiral Axel I. Berg since its creation in 1959. Boris Gnedenko is currently the deputy director of the Council. Day-to-day operations are managed by a presidium to which are attached the following sections which administer the research and engineering projects of the Council:

Realibility Section
Mathematics Section
Information Theory Section
Engineering Section
Measuring Instrument Section
Management and Organizational Section
Juridical Section
Philosophical Section
Linguistics Section
Biological Section
Medical Section

Psychology Section
Transportation Section
Economics Section
Power Systems Section
Chemistry Section

The studies supervised by the Council include analyses of natural and abstract complex dynamic systems to determine the elements operative therein and the communications pathways through which the elements are related systemically; the representation of the elements and their interconnections symbolically; and determination of the decision rules of the system and of the algorithms by which optimal decisions could be made.

The engineering cybernetics studies administered by the Council are concerned with the construction of hardware analysis of the mathematical models constructed by theoretical cyberneticists. In the engineering phase particular emphasis is placed on the application of new physical principles in the construction of technological control systems and on hardware systems that exhibit information-processing behavior analogous to that of the human brain.

Actual research development and engineering studies are carried out in institutes, industrial installations, hospitals, institutions of higher education, and so forth. Perhaps, the most remarkable organizational development consists in the establishment of a number of cybernetics institutes throughout the Soviet Union. The Institute of Automatics and Telemechanics, the largest single research establishment in the USSR, had "Technical Cybernetics" added to its name during 1964.

The translation of theoretical cybernetics research and engineering results into social practice rests with new organizations such as the Interdepartment Scientific Council for the Introduction of Mathematics and Computer Technology into the National Economy (ISC).

The ISC is subordinate to the State Committee for the Coordination of Scientific Research of the Supreme Economic Council and is directed by Academician V. M. Glushkov, a young, brilliant, Lenin-Prize Laureate.[15] The sections of this Council are shown in Fig. 2. The tasks have been defined as follows:

> The creation and introduction of automated systems for the processing of information of state significance on the basis of electronic computing and equipment facilities, including automated systems for planning, accounting and economic administration. The development of computing, control and information–logical machinery, as well as of auxiliary apparatus, ensuring the processing of information in the national economy. The development of a unified documentation system and methods of coding information in the system of the national economy, suitable for processing on electronic computing and other machines.[16]

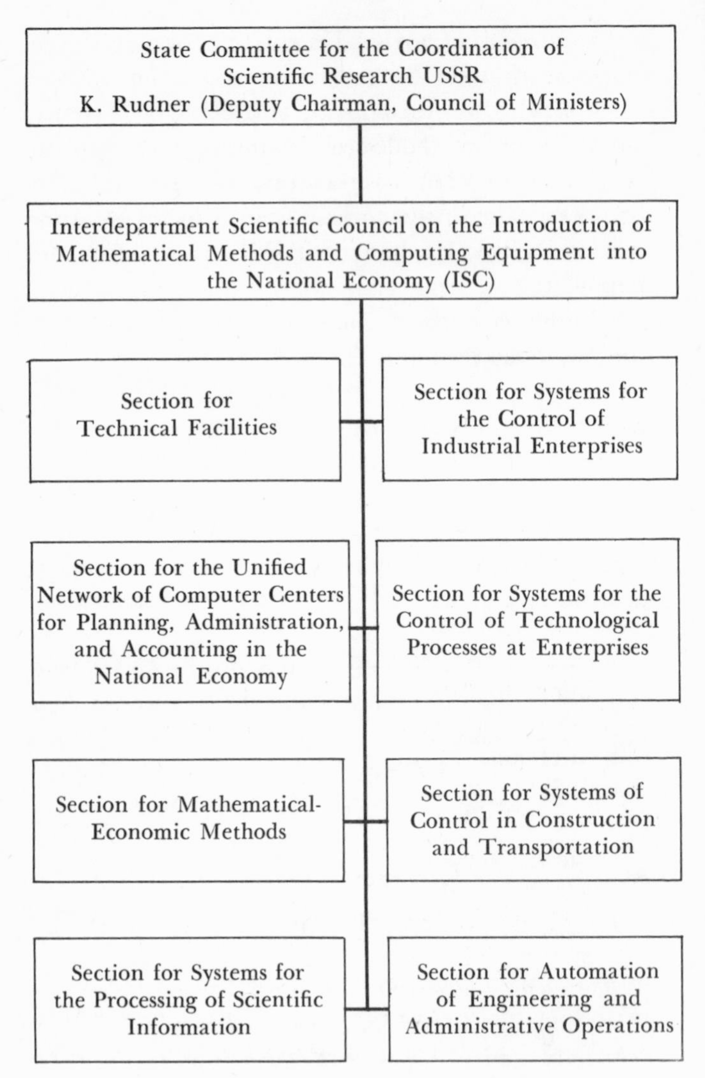

Fig. 2. Organization of the ISC.

Production of actual systems of control is the responsibility of the State Committee for Instrument Building, Automation and Control Systems, subordinate to the State Planning Commission (GOSPLAN). M. Ye. Rakovskiy, its chairman, who could be called "the world's first minister of automation," directs a staff of 250 staff scientists and engineers.

Also established in 1963, along with the groups under Glushkov and Rakovskiy, was the State Committee for Machine Building directed by A. I. Kostousov. This committee controls the more than 70 research institutes concerned with the design and construction of automatic machine tools, presses, woodworking machines, and automatic control equipment for the food, textile, glass, and light industries and for sensing, measuring, and other devices.

Programmed Soviet research on bionics, artificial intelligence, information processing, and so on, has as its objective the installation of "cybernetic factories" by 1973. Because the development of such a level of production technology would have revolutionary implications for society, the Pedagogical Section of the Cybernetics Council is attempting concurrently to develop means for teaching the "New Communist Man" who will live in the world in which such factories will operate. The methodological approaches to the control of the new man's development are fundamentally the same as those that will be used in controlling the cybernetic factories.[17]

To test the idea that ontogenesis is a controllable process, more than two million children have been put into a "boarding school" program since 1956. Using the latest electronic and other "cybernetic teaching methods"[18] for transmitting information to the individual student they hope to control the child's development in consonance with a reference model of what the "Communist Man" ought to be. Legal literature from the USSR describes such efforts as "the formation of the future in the present."[19]

The formal organizational-administrative network and the substantive scientific content of cybernetics are supposed to cofunction in response to national requirements for improved information sensing, processing, storage, and transmission capabilities. These, in turn, will be used in controlling the development of the real world in ways consonant with the reference model for what the future social system is to be. This model seems to be based in some measure at least on the theory of development alluded to earlier, i.e., progress in movement toward higher levels of organizational complication and increased automation of functions. The efficacy of the cybernetic organization, of the interdisciplinary research program, and even of the reference model are being put to a test in the task most important to the cybernetics program: the conceptualization, engineering, and installation of the Unified Information Network of the USSR. This is to be a "nervous system" tying together the systems' "sensors" of internal and external environments at all organizational levels with the highest decision centers. These can then determine optimal courses of action and transmit information to the effector organs of the social system—ministries, production complexes, schools, defense installations, and so on. The new behavior of the system is transmitted to the decision-makers and new actions undertaken in a continuous process analogous to that by which a helmsman steers a ship toward its destination.

Evaluation of the Soviet cybernetics program with its philosophical, scientific, engineering, and social dimensions must await the 1970–75 period when the Unified Information Network is scheduled for completion. Until that time, there will be very little data upon which to base any judgments as to the meaning of the Soviet cybernetics program for international society.

PROSPECTS

When Professor Wiener gave the first account of some of the ethical and sociological aspects of cybernetics, the underlying concepts were relatively new and neither the scientific nor the social implications were entirely clear.[20] Today cybernetics has moved from the status of a program for the future and a "pious hope"[21] to become a working technique in engineering, medicine, sociology, and biology. In the Soviet Union cybernetics has become tantamount to a science of government. In

15 years cybernetics has also undergone a great internal development which will have further implications for the future of societies everywhere.

The current status of cybernetics may be a source of further "pious hopes" for the next 15 years. Foremost is the hope that the impingement of the circle of cybernetic ideas will tend to lessen the chaos and to increase the stability of the international system while fostering the rapid transition of its member states. This hope is rooted in the expectation that cybernetics can amplify human capabilities for dealing with the complexity of the real world. Through the study and engineering of information reception, processing, storage, and transmission in disparate systems and through the development of techniques for using information in control procedures, cybernetics may provide keys to the maintenance of stability in the real world and to the harmoniously directed evolution of each society toward its self-determined concept of the good life.

Realization of this "pious hope" would require more than just scientists and engineers. "Helmsmen" are needed on the ships of state. The present gulf between the scientific, technical, and humanistic cultures and the world of national and international politics may be bridged by the ideas of cybernetics. Perhaps these hopes are unwarranted, and cybernetics is just a straw at which one may grasp in the absence of any other concept on the intellectual horizon that would tie together the notions of stability, change, and goal-seeking necessary to the survival of social systems and, perhaps, of the human species. But it would be a serious mistake to judge *a priori* that cybernetics will provide solutions to the intractable national and international social problems growing out of the sweeping technological revolution of our day. Since the phenomenal rise of science from 1500–1700, thinkers have tried to interpret social processes in the same way that physics interprets natural phenomena and to construct Utopias based on such interpretations. The former efforts led only to such intellectual developments as Comte's social physics, Herbert Spencer's purely physical interpretation of social life, or Gidding's attempt in his *Principles of Sociology* to correlate physical and psychical factors. The latter efforts led to Utopian constructs such as Fourier's Phalanx and Skinner's Walden Two. These intellectual efforts did not foster improvement of society at large to any demonstrable degree. Nor should it be forgotten that Saint-Simon propounded ideas which, in retrospect, sound very much like those of Admiral Berg in his *Cybernetics at the Service of Communism*. It would, however, be mistaken to reject on the basis of historical precedent the possibility that cybernetics might have some potential for solving the problems of modern society.

There are indications that the most powerful nations appreciate this potential and that efforts will be made toward its realization. Soviet efforts to develop and use cybernetics for the management of society have been described. U. S. officials also are acutely aware of the relationship between information and entropy and the implications of that relationship in considerations of the ever increasing complexity and dynamism of our social system. While still a United States Senator, Hubert Humphrey introduced a joint congressional resolution for the creation of the Presidential Advisory Staff for Scientific Information Management with the observation that:

> Whether the United States of America, having reached a climax of achievement, will now begin the process of decline and death may depend to a great extent upon our capacity to assist the responsible decision-makers of Government and industry in assimilating and utilizing our new knowledge to achieve the goals of our democratic society.
>
> If we cannot develop new techniques to master the new knowledge, to better perceive the ultimate nature of our changing institutions, and to assist our policy- and decision-makers in performing their responsibilities, we may be turned down the dusty road to ruin, a road cluttered with the rubble of dim-sighted decisions and poorly programmed policies.
>
> The development of new techniques to aid our decision-makers is, therefore, as much a part of the competition between the United States and the communist world as the space race, or the development of sophisticated military sys-

tems, and is more crucial to the ultimate success of our democratic mission in the world.[22]

The mutual emphasis of the United States and the Soviet Union on the importance of information in government—on the nervous system of society rather than on its muscle—might presage a new kind of international competition during the next 15 years. It might be a race to devise and use techniques at home and abroad for increasing order in the world rather than disorder, harmony rather than chaos, social evolution rather than revolution.

That intervention by intelligent beings can decrease entropy in physical systems was demonstrated by Leo Szilard with mathematical rigor in 1929.[23] Perhaps the availability of techniques for rational intervention in international society are more than just "pious hopes" even at the present time. Certainly the need and rationale for their use are becoming clearer day by day. For example, Lindsay and Margenau have formulated an ethical principle based upon the concepts of thermodynamics and Kant's categorical imperative. This principle, called the "thermodynamic imperative," may constitute the principal ethical implication of cybernetics.

> All men should fight as vigorously as possible to increase the degree of order in their environment, i.e., consume as much entropy as possible, in order to combat the natural tendency for entropy to increase and for order in the universe to be transformed into disorder, in accordance

with the second law of thermodynamics.[24]

The social and ethical implications of cybernetics for the future could have a salutary effect on the nature of social system dynamics. In the face of thermonuclear reality and an underdeveloped world on the brink of revolution, a "race" of the developed nations to "consume entropy" and thereby foster the development of emerging nations might prove to be what William James called "the moral equivalent of war; something heroic that will speak to men as universally as war does, and yet will be compatible with their spiritual selves as war has proved to be incompatible."

NOTES

1. A very interesting account of the intellectual turmoil of this period was written by members of the Eastern Department of the German Social-Democratic Party in Bonn and translated by Barbara J. Ernst in *Rand Memorandum* RM-3078/9-PR (February, 1963).
2. "Draft Program of the CPSU, 1961," *FBIS* (August 11, 1961), p. 47.
3. See, for example, A. N. Kolmogorov, "Automatic Machines and Life Processes," *The Soviet Review* (July, 1962), p. 41.
4. See E. Kol'man, "Chto takoe kibernetika," *Voprosy Filosofii,* 4 (1955).
5. *Filosofskiye voprosy kibernetiki* (Philosophical Problems of Cybernetics) (Moscow: Publishing House of Socio-economic Literature, 1961).
6. "Problems of Cybernetics in the Philosophy Sem-

inars at the Academy of Sciences," *Voprosy Filosofii,* 1 (1961), 150–157.

7. This conference was organized by the Cybernetics Council of the Academy of Sciences, USSR, the Scientific Council on the Philosophical Problems of the Natural Sciences, and the Party Committee of the Presidium of the Academy of Sciences.

8. N. I. Mayzel' and L. V. Fatkin, "Conference on the Philosophical Problems of Cybernetics," *Voprosy Psikhologii,* 5 (1962), 184–191.

9. Admiral Berg's ideas are developed in more detail in a multivolume work, *Cybernetics in the Service of Communism,* of which he is the chief editor. Two volumes have appeared to date.

10. E. A. Arab-Ogly, "Applications of Cybernetics in Social Sciences," *Problemy Filosofii,* 5 (1958), 138–151.

11. *World Marxist Review: The Theoretical and Information Journal of Communist and Workers' Parties,* 6, 4 (1963), 39–48.

12. "Cybernetics, Planning and Social Progress," *USSR* (September, 1964), pp. 8–17.

13. See note 4 above.

14. I. V. Novik, *Kibernetika: Filosofskiye i Sotsiologicheskiye Problemy* (Moscow: State Publishing House for Political Literature, 1963), p. 199.

15. Glushkov is also director of the Institute for Cybernetics in Kiev, the world's first cybernetics institute.

16. *Bvulletin Tekhniki-Ekonomicheskov Informatsii,* 9 (September, 1963).

17. Considering the human nervous system as a "machine" which collects, processes, stores, and transmits information, it is credited with being the bearer

of inheritance of the culture in which the nervous system is imbedded and with which it interacts. Furthermore, the Soviets believe that the adult behavior of an individual is determined in a stochastic manner by the information transactions of the nervous systems of the young.

18. What the Soviets call pedagogical cybernetics is only in the formative stages, although some results have been accomplished in the application of teaching machines. The first Soviet teaching machine was built in 1962 by L. Landa of the Institute of Theory and History of Pedagogy, and S. P. Khlennikov, an engineer. The addition of a memory system in this class of machines is now under development. The theory, development, and techniques for use of such machines is the responsibility of the Commission on Programmed Instruction, Scientific Council of Cybernetics.

19. See A. A. Zhadanov, "Freedom and Law," *Filosofskiye Nauk,* 7, 2 (1964), 14–24.

20. N. Wiener, *The Human Use of Human Beings: Cybernetics and Society* (Boston: Houghton Mifflin Company, 1950).

21. This phrase is used by Norbert Wiener in *God and Golem, Inc.,* p. vii, to describe what he had written in *The Human Use of Human Beings.*

22. *Congressional Record,* September 10, 1964, p. 21284.

23. Leo Szilard, "The Decrease of Entropy in a Thermodynamic System by the Intervention of Intelligent Beings," translation in *Behavioral Science,* vol. 9.

24. R. B. Lindsay, "A Scientific Analogy: The Thermodynamic Imperative," *The Role of Science in Civilization* (New York: Harper & Row, 1963), pp. 290–298.

Notes on the Contributors

Charles R. Dechert, a former Mazzini Fellow at the Johns Hopkins University Bologna Center, is professor of Political Science at Purdue University. Professor Dechert has served as consultant to government commissions and academic institutions both in Italy and the United States. Among his published articles, "Cybernetics and the Human Person" (*International Philosophical Quarterly*) won the Harman Prize in Philosophy in 1964. Also in 1964 he directed the Georgetown University symposium on the Social Impact of Cybernetics.

John Diebold is president and founder of the Diebold Group, Inc., a management consulting firm specializing in the application of technology to government and private enterprise. A pioneer in the field of automation, Mr. Diebold coined the word in its current meaning in his first book. Mr. Diebold has served on numerous government delegations and is a member and director of professional societies in the United States and abroad.

JOHN J. FORD is a government expert on the implications of cybernetics for the maintenance of international security through the guidance of social development. He is Executive Director of the American Society for Cybernetics and a Professorial Lecturer on Societal Cybernetics at the American University, Washington, D.C.

MARSHALL MCLUHAN is Professor at St. Michael's College in the University of Toronto and a Fellow of the Royal Society of Canada. He is well known as a lecturer and the author of numerous articles for journals in the field of literature. His books include *Understanding Media,* published in 1964. In 1963 he was appointed by the President of the University of Toronto to create a new Centre for Culture and Technology.

MAXIM W. MIKULAK is Associate Professor of the History of Science and of Russia at State University College, Fredonia, New York. He is a member of the American Association for the Advancement of Science and other professional societies, and in 1965 was designated New York State Faculty Scholar in International Studies. He has contributed essays and reviews to various journals devoted to his specialties and to several volumes of papers.

ULRIC NEISSER is on the staff of the Unit for Experimental Psychiatry in Philadelphia, affiliated with both the Institute of the Pennsylvania Hospital and the University of Pennsylvania. He is also an Associate Professor at the University, and holds a Career Development Award from the National Institute of Mental Health. A member of the American Psychological Association and other professional societies, Dr. Neisser is the author of numerous papers in psychological journals and of a forthcoming book, *Cognitive Psychology*.

HYMAN G. RICKOVER, Vice Admiral, USN, has been Director, Division of Naval Reactors, U.S. Atomic Energy Commission since 1949. During his directorship the Nautilus, the first nuclear-powered submarine, was designed and built, as was the world's first nuclear power plant exclusively for generation of electricity. His distinguished contributions to the nuclear program, and in other areas, have brought him countless awards, including the Congressional Gold Medal. He has published numerous articles, two reports to the House Appropriations Committee, and three books, including *Education and Freedom* and *American Education —A National Failure*.

ROBERT THEOBALD is an author, lecturer, and consultant concerned with the impact of science and technology on the economy and society. His books include *The Rich and the Poor, The Challenge of Abundance,* and *Free Men and Free Markets.* He has edited *The Guaranteed Income* and is presently completing a book entitled *Cybernetic Economics.*

Index